HANDWRITING 6

SECOND EDITION

bju press
Greenville, South Carolina

WORKTEXT HIGHLIGHTS

Theme:	People and Professions
Letter Styles:	BJU Press Cursive Alphabet Chancery Style of Calligraphy
Skills Emphasized:	Good Handwriting Posture Letter Formation Slant Consistency Alignment Spacing Neatness
Evaluation:	Pretest Self-evaluations Weekly Assessments Post-test

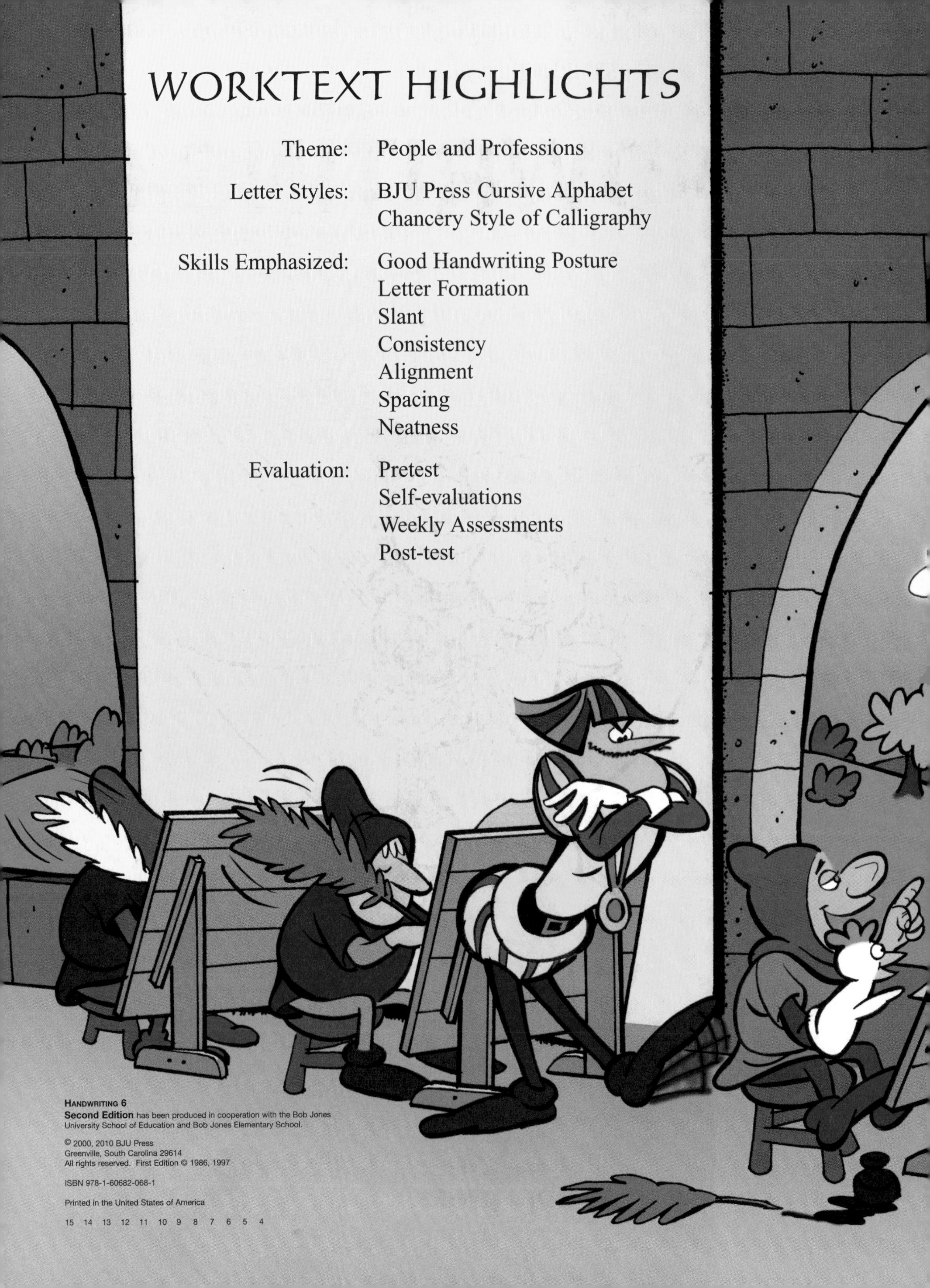

HANDWRITING 6
Second Edition has been produced in cooperation with the Bob Jones University School of Education and Bob Jones Elementary School.

ISBN 978-1-60682-068-1

Printed in the United States of America

15 14 13 12 11 10 9 8 7 6 5 4

WORKTEXT CONTENTS

Here's Penfellow, from the Dark Ages,
A scribe who's not earning his wages;
Chanticleer is his friend
But no help in the end
For their daydreaming doesn't fill pages!

Consultants:
Grace C. Hargis, Ph.D.
James R. Davis, M.A.
Walter G. Fremont, Ed.D.
Melva M. Heintz, M.A.
Janice A. Joss, M.A.T.
Philip D. Smith, Ed.D.

Revision Coordinator:
Joyce Garland

Developed by:
Charlene Killian
Susan I. Lehman

Illustrator:
Dana Thompson

Typesetter:
Janet Davis

Designer:
Elly Kalagayan

Editor:
Carolyn Cooper

Revision Graphics:
Janet Davis

Words to Work By

"The door to the room of success swings on the hinges of opposition."

"The test of your character is what it takes to stop you."

"You can do anything you ought to do."

"Blessed is the man who knows how to make stepping stones out of stumbling stones."

—taken from "Chapel Sayings of Dr. Bob Jones Sr."

Pretest

name____________________

Write the quotations.

Digital Numerals

name________________________

1 2 3 4 5 6 7 8 9 0

Answer the questions about the pictures, using the above numeral formations.

PhotoDisc, Inc.

What is the telephone number showing on the phone?

____

____

PhotoDisc, Inc.

What is the time of the flight that was cancelled?

____

____

PhotoDisc, Inc.

What is the total shown on the calculator?

____

____

PhotoDisc, Inc.

What is the time shown on the computer screen?

____

____

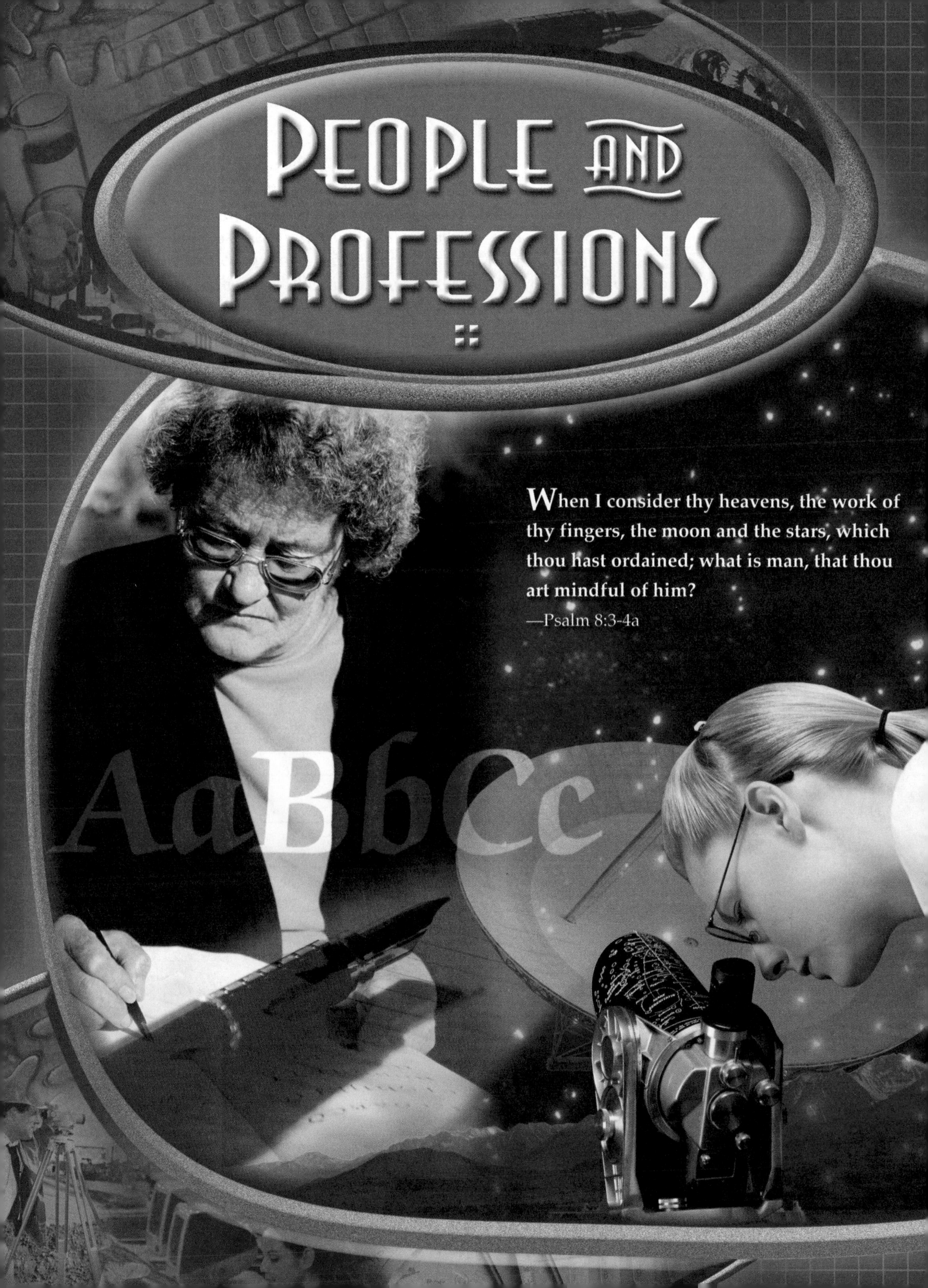
PEOPLE AND PROFESSIONS
When I consider thy heavens, the work of thy fingers, the moon and the stars, which thou hast ordained; what is man, that thou art mindful of him?
—Psalm 8:3-4a
AaBbCc

The Calligrapher's Terminology

name________________________

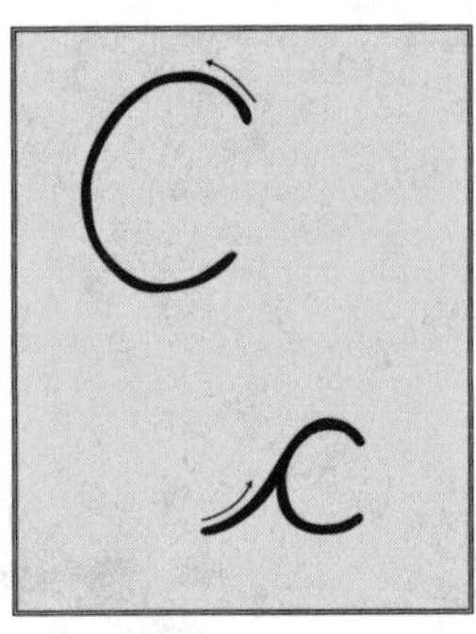

As early as the third century A.D., it was recorded that scribes noted for the speed and beauty of their handwriting often accompanied great men on their journeys.

Contemporary scribes called calligraphers also engage in the art of fine handwriting. They are often employed by printers and publishers who recognize the beauty of their work.

Write the lettering term and its definition.

hook—a curved ending and beginning to strokes of an alphabet

pen nib—the removable tip of a lettering pen or fountain pen

swashes—long, decorative additions to letters

vellum—a fine grade of parchment paper prepared from lambskin, kidskin, or calfskin

The Astronomer's Telescopes

name____________________

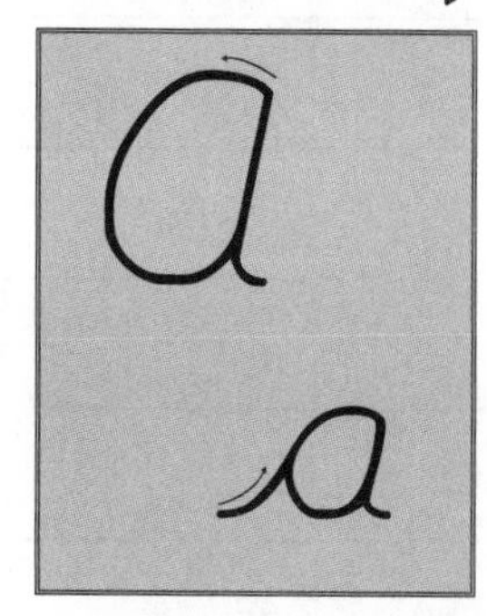

Using powerful telescopes, astronomers study the sun, moons, and planets in our solar system. They are also able to observe distant galaxies and stars. With what they observe, they are able to predict events such as eclipses, comet sightings, and even the interference of sunspots on our communication systems.

Write the information about two of the world's largest telescopes.

NASA

The Hubble telescope orbits the earth and allows views of space that are unavailable from telescopes on the earth's surface.

This is an aerial view of the world's largest fixed-dish radio telescope, located near Arecibo, Puerto Rico.

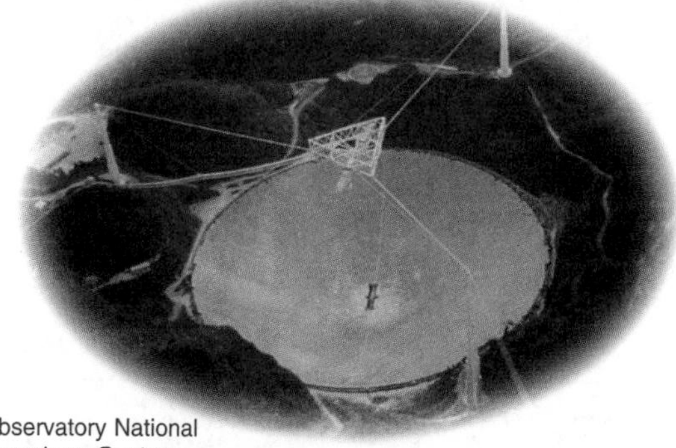

Arecibo Radio Observatory National Astronomy & Ionosphere Center

An Astronomical Task

name________________________

Handwriting Tips

Alignment is the correct placement of letters in relation to the base line.

~~c a~~ c a

Write the letters and words, using correct alignment.

C C

c c

calligrapher

A A

a a

astronomer

Alphabetize each column of words on the lines below.

celestial	angle	reflector
comet	alignment	refractor
cluster	ascender	meteor
cosmology	alphabet	galaxy
chromatic	accuracy	planet

The Lights in the Heavens

name________________________

Self-evaluation

	s	n
Posture		
Paper Positioning		
Pencil Hold		
Letter Formation		
Alignment		
Slant		
Spacing		
Neatness		

s=satisfactory n=needs improvement

"And God made two great lights; the greater light to rule the day, and the lesser light to rule the night: he made the stars also."

—Genesis 1:16

"He telleth the number of the stars; he calleth them all by their names."

Psalm 147:4

"Which maketh Arcturus, Orion, and Pleiades, and the chambers of the south. Which doeth great things past finding out; yea, and wonders without number."

Job 9:9–10

Write the verses on the lines below.

Calligraphy Letters c and a

name________________________

c a

Calligraphy Tips

Concentrate on using the proper pen hold, paper position, and body position.

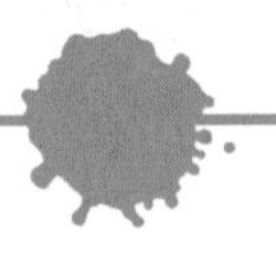

Copy the practice strokes.

Write the letters *c* and *a*.

c c c

a a a

Use with Lesson 6.

People and Professions

They that go down to the sea in ships, that do business in great water; these see the works of the Lord, and his wonders in the deep.
—Psalm 107:23-24

Over the Ocean Blue

name____________________

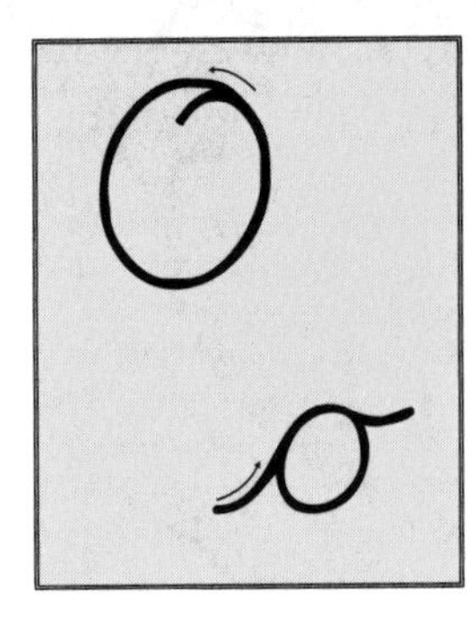

A scientist who studies the ocean is called an oceanographer. He often works on a research ship equipped with special instruments. An oceanographer studies the waves, currents, and tides of the ocean.

Write the following paragraphs about the ocean on handwriting paper.

The waves of the ocean move up and down. When a wave reaches the shore, the bottom of the wave begins to drag, and the top of the wave falls forward.

The waters in the ocean move in streams called currents. The flow of the currents is caused by the earth's rotation.

Quarrying for Granite

name________________________

A quarrier digs, cuts, and blasts stone in an open pit, or quarry.

Vermont Travel Division

Write the outline on handwriting paper.

I. Crushed stone
  A. Procedure for crushing stone
    1. Explosives set off in holes
    2. Stone crushed in crusher plant
  B. Purposes for crushed stone
    1. Used in concrete
    2. Used in road building
II. Dimension stone
  A. Procedure for cutting stone
    1. Large blocks cut by machine
    2. Small blocks cut with wedges
  B. Purposes for cut stone
    1. Used in buildings
    2. Used in monuments

A Puzzle of Professions

name________________________

Write the letters and words. Watch for descenders.

O O

o o

oceanographer

Q Q

q q

quarrier

Complete the crossword puzzle using the quarrying words down and the oceanography words across.

Across

2. the rise and fall of the ocean
5. set in motion by the wind
7. a scientist who studies the ocean
8. ocean water that moves in a stream

Down

1. a workman in a quarry
3. stone cut into blocks
4. substance in a quarry
6. stone used for road building

stone crushed
waves quarrier
current tides
oceanographer
dimension

Sea Captain, Then Hymn Writer

name________________________

Self-evaluation

	s	n
Posture		
Paper Positioning		
Pencil Hold		
Letter Formation		
Alignment		
Slant		
Spacing		
Neatness		

s=satisfactory n=needs improvement

Saved from sins of cruelty and greed and called out from a miserable life as a slave-ship captain, John Newton wrote "Amazing Grace" because he knew that his life was in God's hands. This famous hymn has three stanzas that speak of God's grace in salvation, His grace in keeping His children from sin, and His grace in bringing His children safely to heaven.

Write the hymn on handwriting paper.

Amazing Grace

Amazing grace! how sweet the sound,
That saved a wretch like me!
I once was lost, but now am found,
Was blind, but now I see.

'Twas grace that taught my heart to fear,
And grace my fears relieved;
How precious did that grace appear
The hour I first believed!

Thro' many dangers, toils, and snares,
I have already come,
'Tis grace hath bro't me safe thus far,
And grace will lead me home.

Calligraphy Letters o and e

name_______________________________

o e

Calligraphy Tips

Perform strokes in the correct order and start and finish each stroke in the proper place.

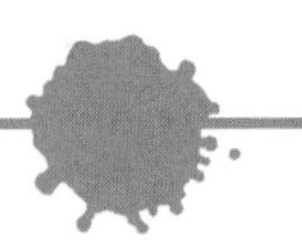

Copy the practice strokes.

Write the letters *o* and *e*.

o o o

e e e

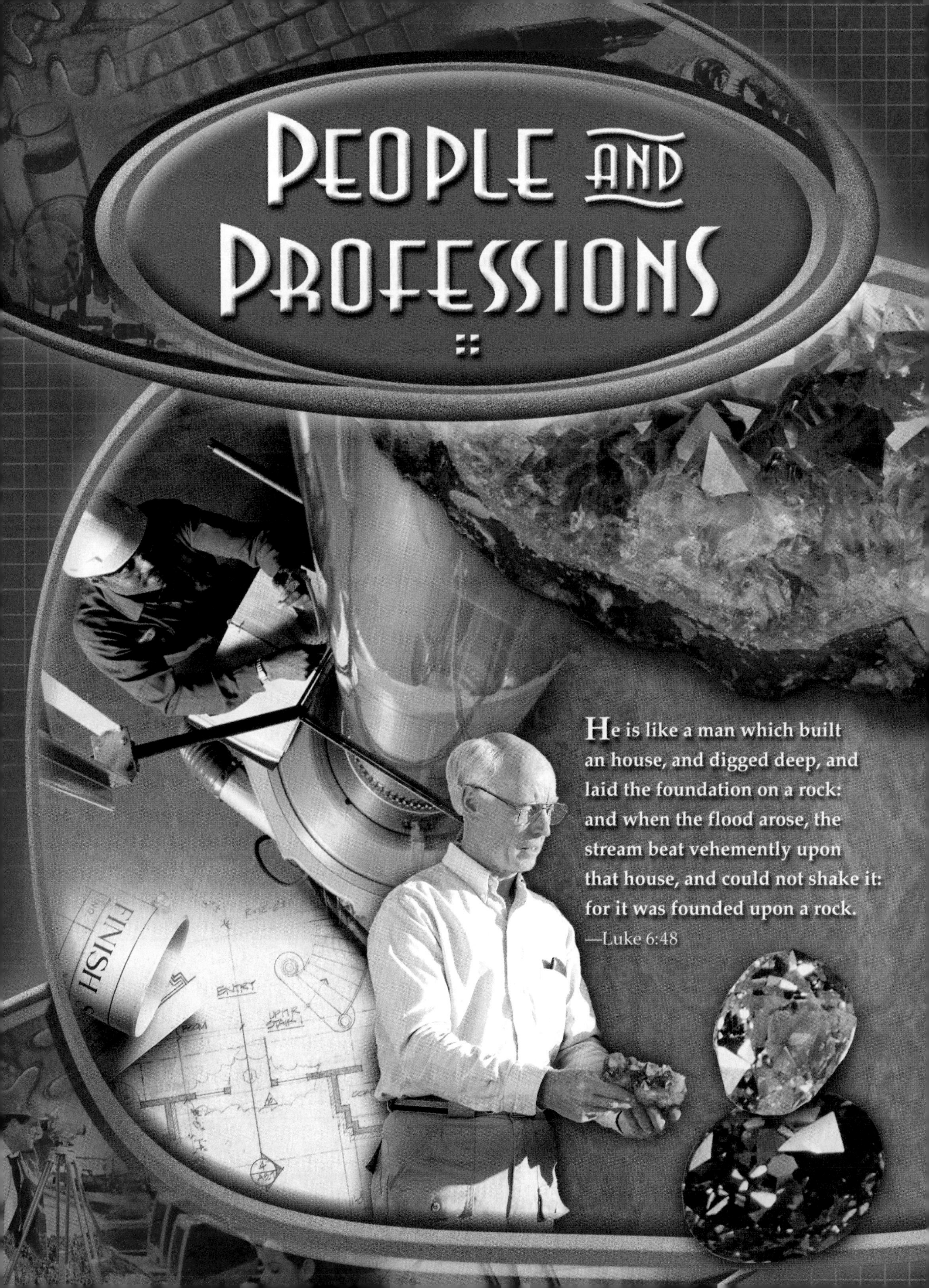
PEOPLE AND PROFESSIONS
He is like a man which built an house, and digged deep, and laid the foundation on a rock: and when the flood arose, the stream beat vehemently upon that house, and could not shake it: for it was founded upon a rock.
—Luke 6:48
FINISH
ENTRY

Rock Hounds

name________________________

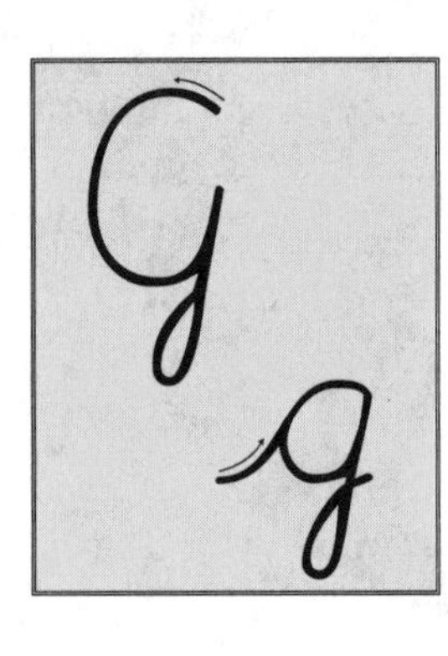

A petrographer, a geologist who describes and classifies rocks, often goes by the slang name of "rock hound." Although not petrographers for pay, many young people and adults spend their spare time as rock hounds too, making their own collections for display.

Write the heading for each list. Then alphabetize each list of rocks.

Igneous
- granite
- pumice
- basalt
- obsidian

Sedimentary
- conglomerate
- shale
- limestone
- coal

Metamorphic
- marble
- slate
- gneiss
- quartzite

Use with Lesson 12.

Time Line Engineering

name____________________

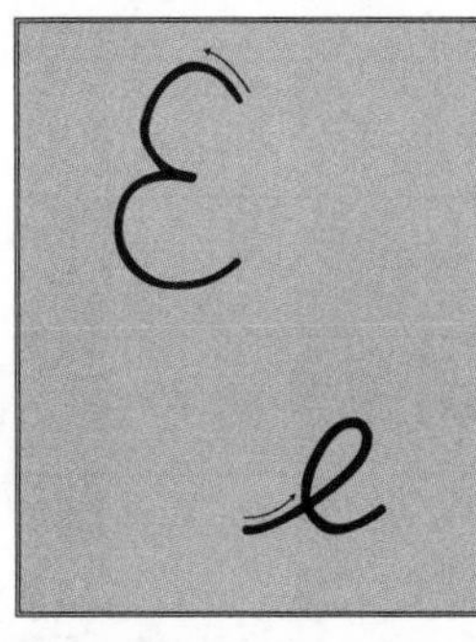

Engineering is the science of making power and materials work for man. Civil engineering, the oldest branch of this science, is concerned with turning power and materials into modern conveniences. Civil engineers plan buildings, bridges, streets, railroads, tunnels, canals, and airports.

Write the dates and the corresponding engineering projects on the lines below in descending chronological order.

1209 London Bridge
1889 Eiffel Tower
80 Colosseum
312 B.C. Appian Aqueduct
432 B.C. Parthenon
1869 Suez Canal
1000 B.C. Solomon's Temple
3000 B.C. Great Pyramid
1965 Verrazano-Narrows Bridge
1883 Brooklyn Bridge

A Geological Engineer

name________________________

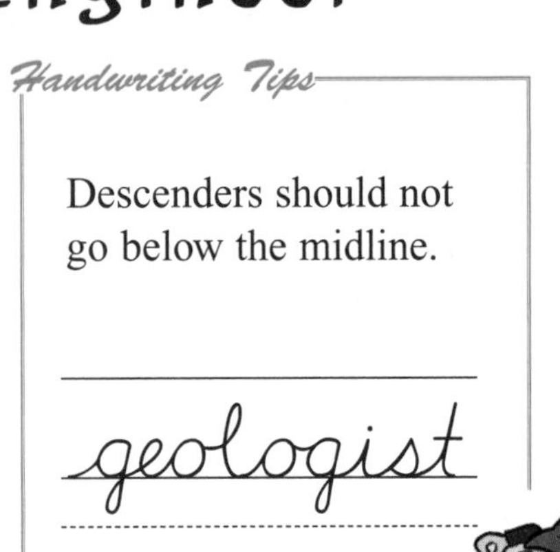

Write the letters and words. Remember to write descenders correctly.

A geological engineer explores the ground for mineral deposits. You are not a geological engineer, but you can explore the ground for rocks and minerals too. You will need a few tools for your exploration.

Write the name of each tool.

mineral hammer

chisel

magnifying glass

pocket magnet

streak plate

pocketknife

Bridge Building

name________________

The Brooklyn Bridge was completed in 1883, fourteen years after construction on it had begun. At the time of its construction, no larger suspension bridge had ever been built. Its designer, John Roebling, did not live to see it completed. He died in 1869, only one year into construction.

His son, Washington Roebling, became chief engineer of the bridge. But he, too, became seriously ill and could not leave his bed. Refusing to quit, he set up a telescope in his bedroom and watched the construction process, sending orders and directions to the foremen and engineers at the site.

Self-evaluation

	s	n
Posture		
Paper Positioning		
Pencil Hold		
Letter Formation		
Alignment		
Slant		
Spacing		
Neatness		

s=satisfactory n=needs improvement

PhotoDisc, Inc. www.arttoday.com Library of Congress

Write the facts about the Brooklyn Bridge on handwriting paper.

- The Brooklyn Bridge connects Brooklyn and Manhattan.
- It was the largest suspension bridge in the world when it was completed in 1883.
- The bridge's span over the river is 1,595 feet.
- Towering 276 feet high, the bridge hangs from steel cables, some of them almost 16 inches thick.
- There are four cables, each one weighing 1,732,086 pounds.
- The total cost of its construction was 15 million dollars.

Calligraphy Letters
m and *n*

name______________________

m n

Calligraphy Tips

Use the most space between two straight strokes; use a little less space between a straight and a curved stroke; and use the least space between two curved strokes.

Copy the practice strokes.

Write the letters *m* and *n*.

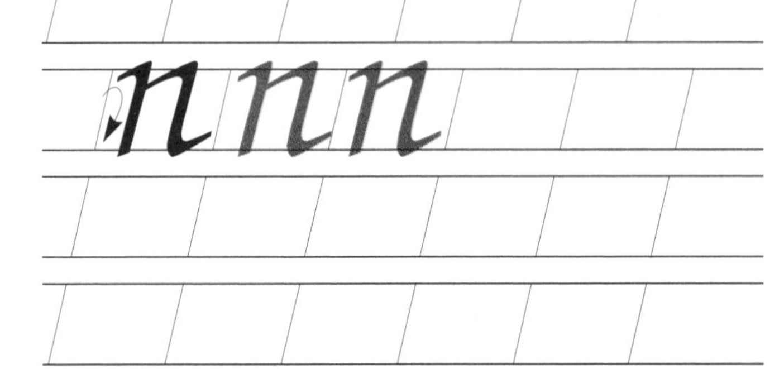

Use with Lesson 16.

PEOPLE AND PROFESSIONS
For he cometh to judge the earth: he shall judge the world with righteousness, and the people with his truth.
—Psalm 96:13b

Inventors and Their Inventions

name________________________

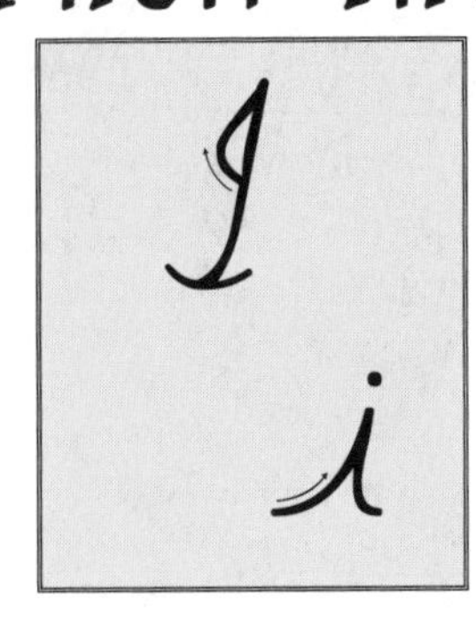

An inventor uses ideas and materials to make something that did not exist before. He is curious about the world around him and strives to meet the needs he sees in the world.

Put the dates in order to make a chronological list of inventions and inventors.

1876—Alexander Graham Bell
1903—Wright Brothers
1793—Eli Whitney
1846—Walter Hunt
1839—Louis Daguerre
1845—Elias Howe

cotton gin

photography

sewing machine

safety pin

telephone

airplane

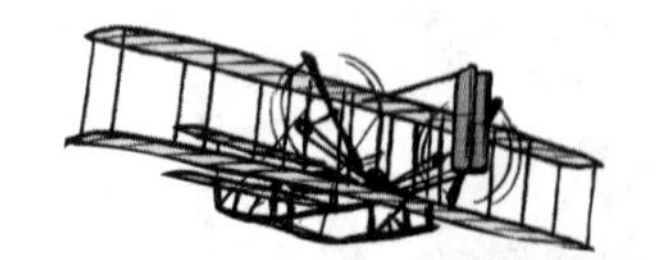

1. 1793—cotton gin
   Eli Whitney
2. ____________________
3. ____________________
4. ____________________
5. ____________________
6. ____________________

Order in the Court

name________________________

A judge is a public official who hears and decides cases in a court of law. The judge decides the questions of law in a trial, while the jury decides the questions of fact. The judge in a trial also pronounces the sentence of the court.

Write the titles of the people in the courtroom in alphabetical order on the lines.

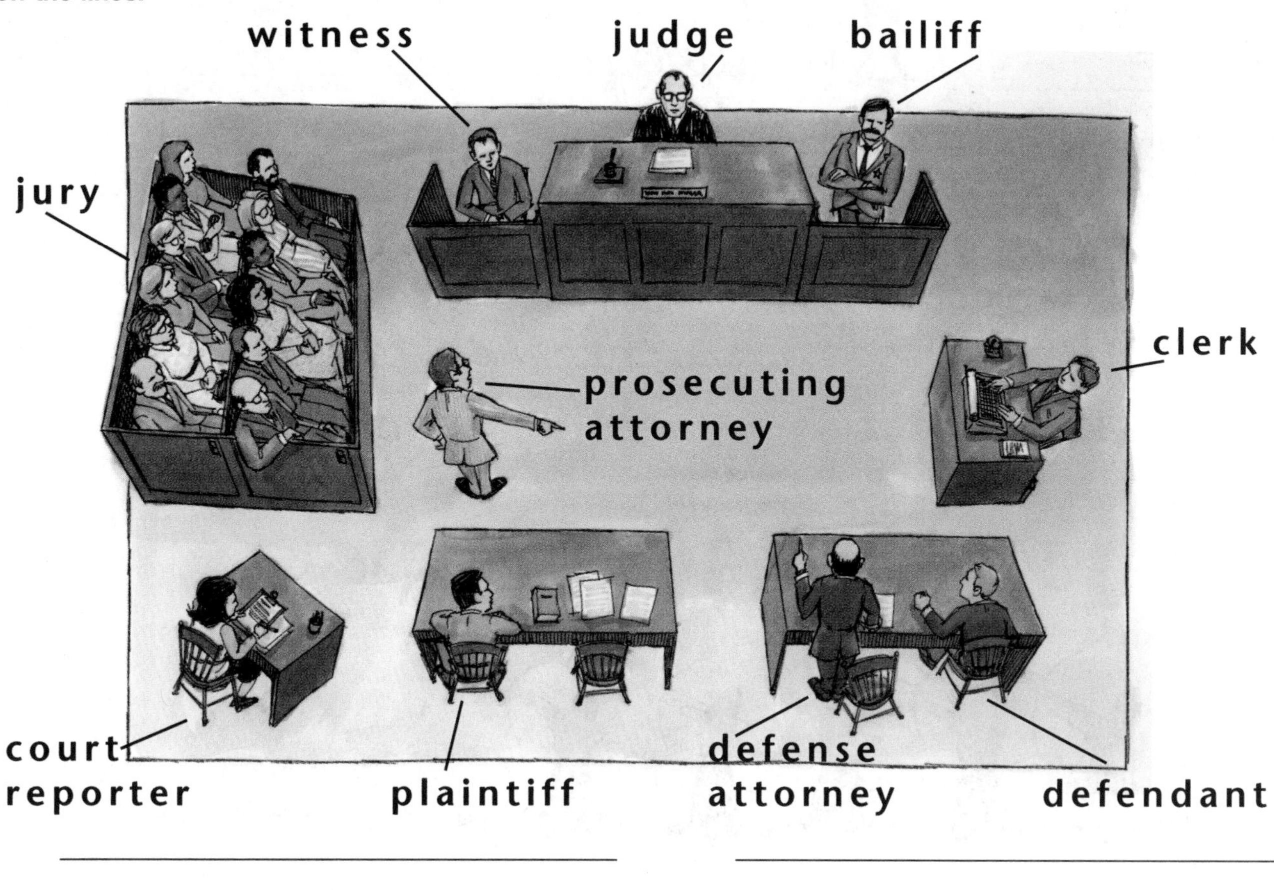

1. ______________________
2. ______________________
3. ______________________
4. ______________________
5. ______________________
6. ______________________
7. ______________________
8. ______________________
9. ______________________
10. ______________________

Every Work into Judgment

name____________________

Handwriting Tips

Cross and dot letters after writing the entire word.

inventor

Write the letters and words.

I I

i i

inventor

J J

j j

judge

Write the verses on handwriting paper.

"And he made in Jerusalem engines, invented by cunning men, to be on the towers and upon the bulwarks, to shoot arrows and great stones withal."

II Chronicles 26:15a

"For God shall bring every work into judgment, with every secret thing, whether it be good, or whether it be evil."

Ecclesiastes 12:14

The Wizard of Menlo Park

name________________________

Self-evaluation

	s	n
Posture		
Paper Positioning		
Pencil Hold		
Letter Formation		
Alignment		
Slant		
Spacing		
Neatness		

s=satisfactory n=needs improvement

In 1868, Thomas Edison invented the electric vote-recording machine. After Congress refused to use the invention, Mr. Edison promised himself that he would never again invent anything that was not wanted or needed. Sixty years later, Thomas Edison had patented more than eleven hundred inventions.

Eastman Chemicals Division

Write the paragraph on handwriting paper.

Thomas Edison's favorite invention was the phonograph. He invented it in 1877 in his Menlo Park laboratory. The phonograph record was a metal cylinder covered with tin foil. A needle recorded the sound waves as small dents in the tin foil. Another needle played back the sounds. The first words recorded and played on Edison's phonograph were "Mary had a little lamb."

Calligraphy Letters
v and *w*

name________________________

Check your pen angle:
Your diagonal strokes will be thin if your pen angle is 45°.

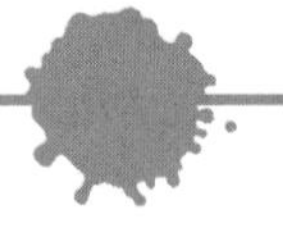

Copy the practice strokes.

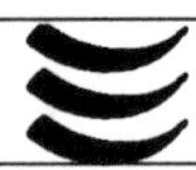

Write the letters *v* and *w*.

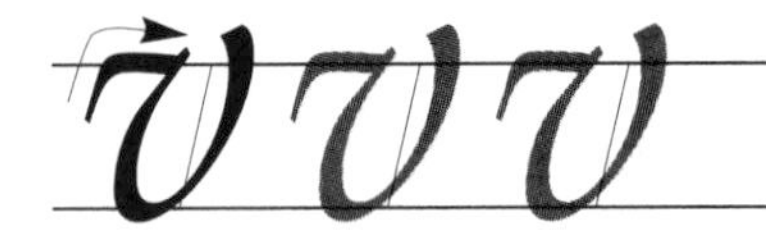

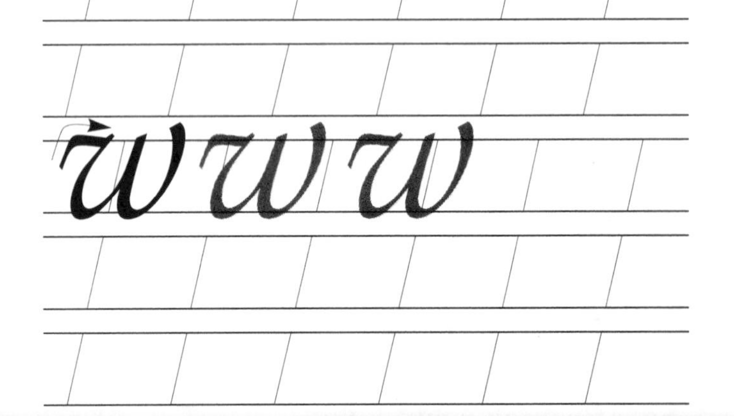

PEOPLE AND PROFESSIONS

When Jesus heard it, he saith unto them, They that are whole have no need of the physician, but they that are sick: I came not to call the righteous, but sinners to repentance.
—Mark 2:17

Word "Searchery"

name________________________

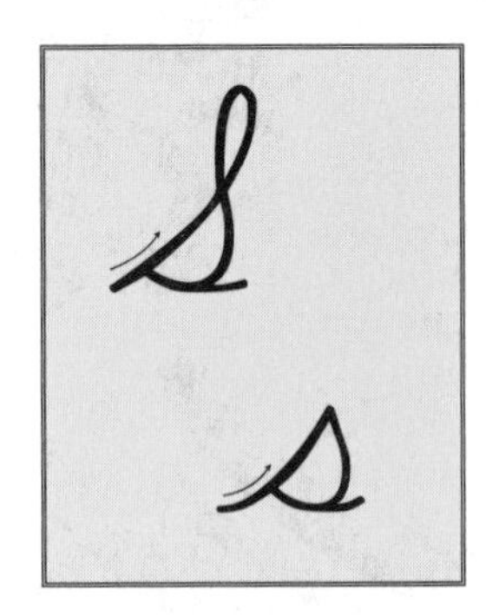

Surgeons treat disease and injury by operating on the affected parts of a person's body. A surgeon never operates alone but is part of a surgical team that includes a first assistant, an anesthesiologist, and a nurse.

Circle the surgeon's supplies and the anesthesiologist's supplies. On handwriting paper, write the surgeon's supplies in one column and the anesthesiologist's supplies in another column.

DOWN—Surgeon's Supplies

scissors
scalpels
sponges
clamps
needles
sutures

ACROSS—Anesthesiologist's Supplies

anesthetics
drugs
masks
oxygen
stethoscope
syringes

A	C	S	T	E	T	H	O	S	C	O	P	E	A	E	I
E	I	U	K	Q	S	Y	B	P	F	J	N	R	V	Z	S
G	T	T	S	Q	U	Y	F	O	X	Y	G	E	N	H	G
M	X	U	C	P	V	X	Z	N	A	S	K	B	E	Z	E
S	Y	R	I	N	G	E	S	G	X	P	H	T	E	X	C
O	C	E	S	K	M	L	C	E	W	D	G	L	D	V	L
I	G	S	S	O	Q	M	A	S	K	S	O	K	L	T	A
W	K	O	O	E	G	C	L	Z	T	I	C	M	E	R	M
D	O	J	R	Y	V	U	P	H	R	V	Q	S	S	P	P
J	S	L	S	R	A	N	E	S	T	H	E	T	I	C	S
L	W	R	J	O	N	M	L	J	I	F	E	B	A	N	C
P	S	F	D	R	U	G	S	O	B	Y	W	U	S	Q	A

A Dental Diagram

name________________________

D d

Doctors who treat diseases of the teeth and the mouth are called dentists. Some dentists operate on the mouth and jaw and remove teeth. Others make replacements for teeth. Deformities of the teeth and the mouth are corrected by dentists called orthodontists.

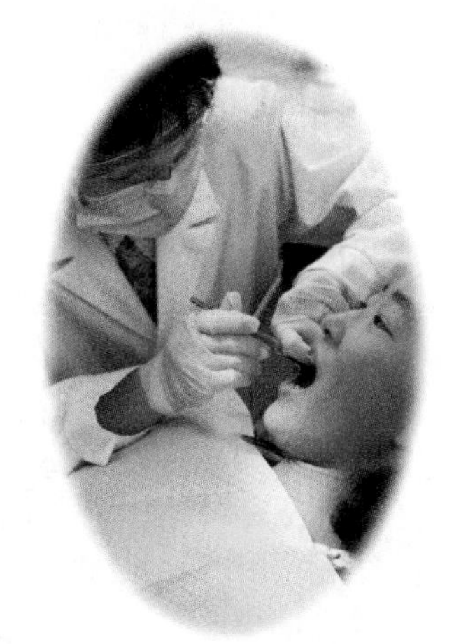
PhotoDisc, Inc.

Write the part of the tooth and the description on handwriting paper.

crown–grows above the gum
root–grows in the socket in the jawbone
neck–connects the crown and the root
enamel–covers the crown
dentin–forms the body of the tooth
pulp–contains tissues, nerves, and blood vessels
cementum–is the protective covering of the root

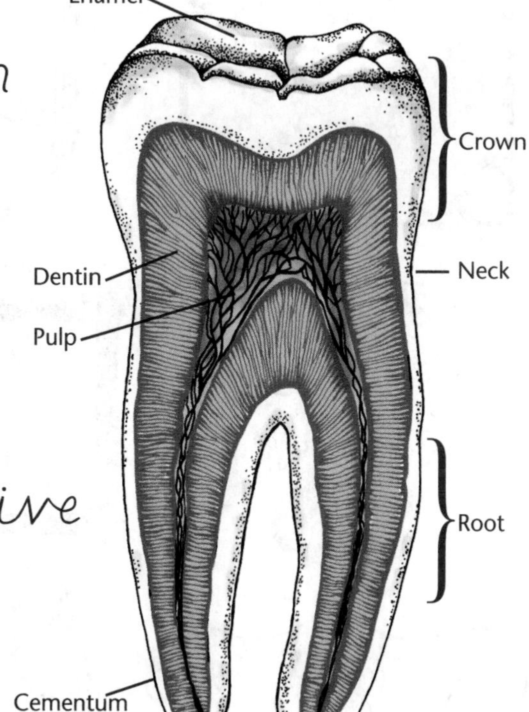

Signs of the Time

name________________________

Write the letters and words.

Handwriting Tips

Correct spacing between words is essential to legible handwriting.

S S

s s

surgeon

D D

d d

dentist

Many achievements in dentistry were made during the 1800s. The first dental school opened in Baltimore, Maryland, in 1839; during the years that followed, several dental clinics were established in the United States. Dentists used signs similar to the following to advertise.

Write the following sign captions on handwriting paper.

Free
Estimates

Painless
Fillings

Crowns Are
Our
Specialty

Reasonable
Charges

Gold
Fillings
$1.00

All
Operations
Painless

Teeth
Extracted
Without Pain

The Great Physician

name________________________

Self-evaluation	s	n
Posture		
Paper Positioning		
Pencil Hold		
Letter Formation		
Alignment		
Slant		
Spacing		
Neatness		

s=satisfactory n=needs improvement

Write the paragraph on handwriting paper.

Four men carried a man sick of the palsy to a house where Jesus was preaching. The men let down the man through the roof. Jesus told the man that his sins had been forgiven and to get up, take his bed, and walk. The man did as Jesus told him and was healed.

Calligraphy Letters
u, i, and r

name____________________

u i r

Calligraphy Tips 

Check your pen angle:
Your serifs at the beginning and end of each letter will be at a 45° angle if your pen angle is 45°.

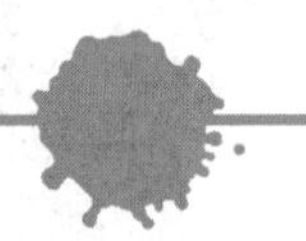

Copy the practice strokes.

Write the letters *u, i,* and *r*.

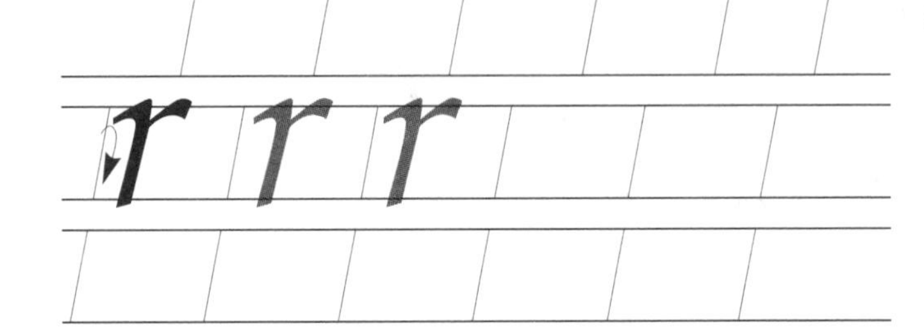

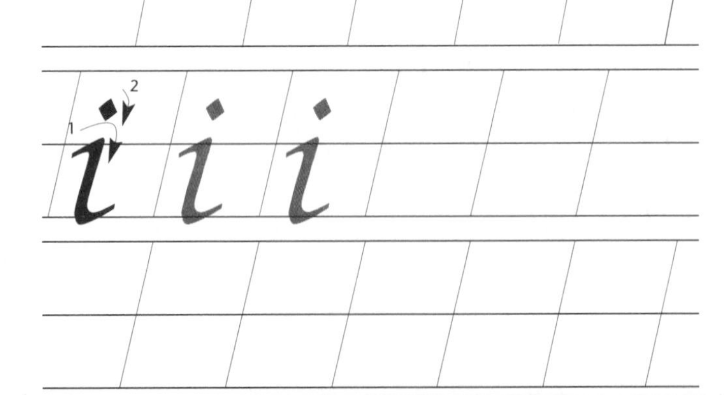

Use with Lesson 26.

PEOPLE AND PROFESSIONS

And Jesus, walking by the sea of Galilee, saw two brethren, Simon called Peter, and Andrew his brother, casting a net into the sea: for they were fishers. And he saith unto them, Follow me, and I will make you fishers of men.

—Matthew 4:18-19

Sew—Sew

name____________________

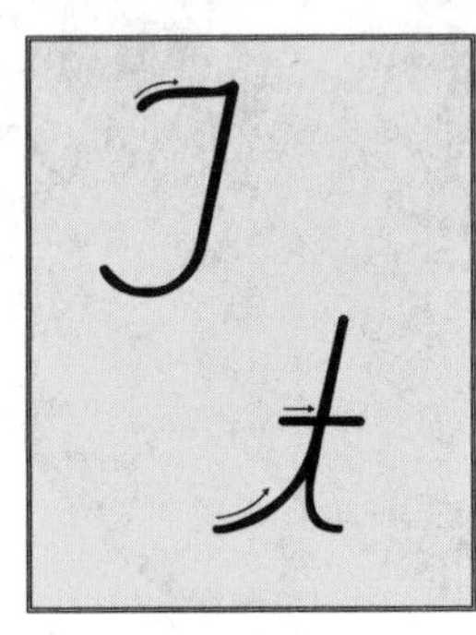

Tailors make, repair, and alter clothing. Most tailors measure customers, fit or make patterns, and then sew garments. Once tailoring was a common profession; but with the invention of sewing machines and mass production of clothing, it has decreased in popularity. However, some people still earn their living making hand-tailored clothes.

A tailor uses many sewing tools. Write the names of the tools on the handwriting lines.

sewing machine
needles
thimble
tape measure
pins
iron
thread
scissors

Tailors must also use fastenings on the garments they make. Write the name of the fastener below each picture.

button hook and eye zipper snap

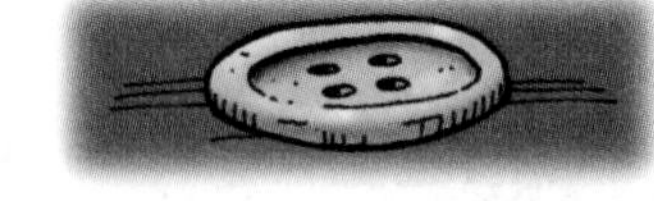

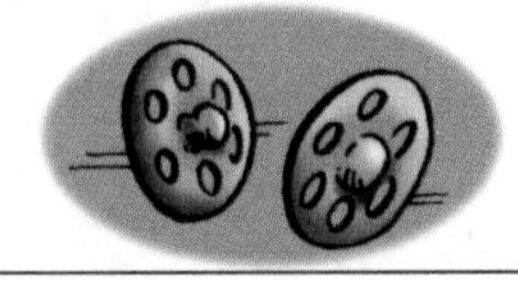

Fish Stories

name____________________

Some people fish for a living, using small boats equipped with nets. They sell their catches to fish canneries or fish markets. But most people fish for sport, using only a rowboat and a single line. In spite of this quiet pastime, sport fishermen are known for their exciting stories and can usually be called on to tell about "the one that got away."

Write funny captions for the cartoons.

Seven at One Blow

name________________________

Write the letters and words.

Handwriting Tips

Margins are imaginary lines on both sides of your paper.

T T

t t

tailor

F F

f f

fisherman

Write the sentences in sequential order on handwriting paper.

- The clever tailor caused a fight to start between two giants.
- The tailor sewed the words "seven at one blow" on his belt.
- Two giants beat the tailor's bed.
- The giant squeezed water out of a rock.
- The tailor killed seven flies at one blow.
- The king's daughter and the tailor married and lived happily ever after.
- The king told the tailor to prove his bravery by killing the giants.

There Were Twelve Disciples

name______________________

Self-evaluation	s	n
Posture		
Paper Positioning		
Pencil Hold		
Letter Formation		
Alignment		
Slant		
Spacing		
Neatness		

s=satisfactory n=needs improvement

Before they became fishers of men, some of Jesus' disciples fished along the Sea of Galilee. When Jesus called Simon Peter and Andrew, they were at work fishing in the sea. James and John, the sons of Zebedee, were mending their nets when Jesus called them to follow Him. These men left everything behind to follow and live with Christ.

Write the names of Jesus' disciples on the lines.

Simon Peter
Andrew
James
John
Philip
Thomas
Matthew
James
Thaddeus
Simon
Judas Iscariot
Bartholomew

Write the names of the four disciples who were fishermen.

Calligraphy Letters *s* and *t*

name________________________

s t

Leave a space of an "o" between words.

Copy the practice strokes.

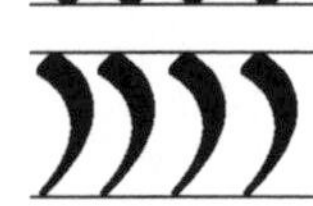

Write the letters *s* and *t*.

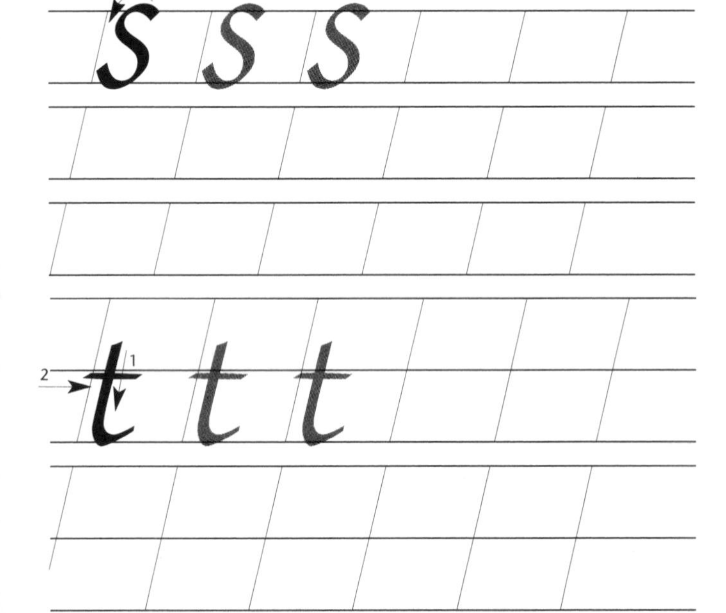

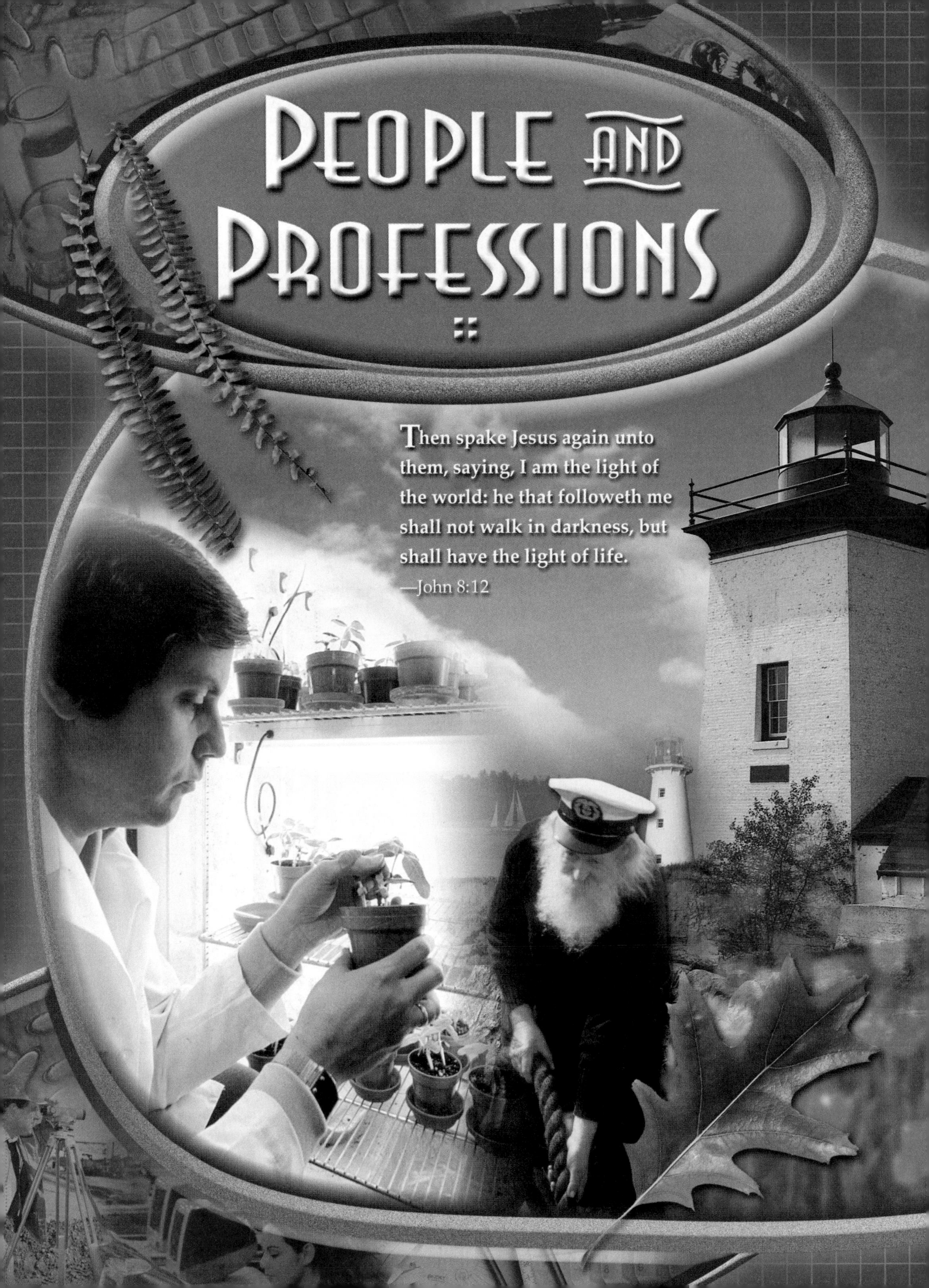
PEOPLE AND PROFESSIONS
Then spake Jesus again unto them, saying, I am the light of the world: he that followeth me shall not walk in darkness, but shall have the light of life.
—John 8:12

Abbie Burgess, Lighthouse Keeper

name________________________

When Abbie Burgess was fourteen years old, her father was appointed the keeper of the two lighthouses on Matinicus Rock, a rock island twenty-two miles from the coast of Maine. Because the lighthouse lamps had to keep burning all night, Abbie tended the lighthouses whenever her father went to the coast for supplies. Although she was only fourteen years old, she managed to keep the lamps lit to protect the passing ships.

Write on handwriting paper the list of things Abbie had to do each morning to get the lamps ready to be lit at night.

1. Blow out the oil lamps in the tower.
2. Remove the glass chimneys after they cool.
3. Clean the oil lamp bowls.
4. Trim the wicks in the lamps.
5. Refill the lamps with oil.
6. Polish the silver reflectors in the tower.

Petit Manan National Wildlife Refuge

First and Last Names

name_______________

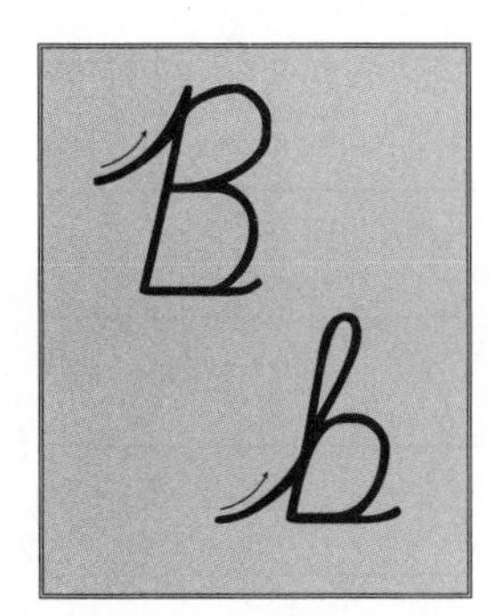

*Botanists study plants. One type of botanist, called a taxonomist, identifies and classifies plants. Taxonomy has been organized along the principles laid out by Carl Linnaeus, who is called "the father of modern taxonomy." He organized all plants by two names—*genus*, meaning "group," and* species*, meaning "kind."*

Write on handwriting paper the genus and species names listed beside each plant.

Acer rubrum (red maple)

Prunus persica (peach)

Zea mays (corn)

Citrus paradisi (grapefruit)

Musa acuminata (banana)

Pisum sativum (green pea)

Picea pungens (blue spruce)

Malus sylvestris (red apple)

Big and Bright

name________________________

Handwriting Tips

Indent the beginning of every paragraph.

The Portland Head Light is the oldest . . .

Write the letters and words.

L L

l l

lighthouse

B B

b b

botanist

Write the paragraphs on handwriting paper. Remember to indent the paragraph.

The Portland Head Light, built in 1791, is the oldest lighthouse on the Maine coast. It rises over a hundred feet above the water at high tide.

Victoria regia is the name of a giant water lily found in northern South America. Each circular floating leaf is six feet across. The flowers are more than a foot across and bloom only two succesive nights a year.

Corel Corporation

Use with Lesson 34.

Report: Old Lighthouses of Maine

name________________________

Self-evaluation	s	n
Posture		
Paper Positioning		
Pencil Hold		
Letter Formation		
Alignment		
Slant		
Spacing		
Neatness		

s=satisfactory n=needs improvement

Steve's class had been learning about Maine in their Heritage Studies class. When his teacher told the class to choose a topic of interest about Maine and write a report about it, Steve immediately knew the topic of his report. He could not wait to find out more about the old lighthouses of Maine!

On handwriting paper, write the bibliography of the reference materials Steve used to write his report about lighthouses in Maine.

Bibliography

"A Strong Tower," Portstown News, January 12, 1996.

Blackmore, Thomas. The First Lighthouse in America.

Jackson, James. Famous Lighthouse Keepers.

"Lighthouses." The National Encyclopedia. 1997, XIII, 45–47.

"Maine." The National Encyclopedia. 1997, XIII, 192–221.

"The Keepers of the Maine Coast." Oceans and Seas, 1999.

Calligraphy Letters *x* and *z*

name______________________

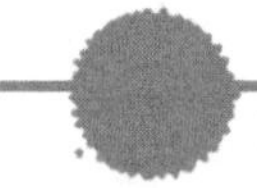

Protect your pen:
Do not apply too much pressure when you are writing.
Replace the cap on your pen when you are not writing.

Copy the practice strokes.

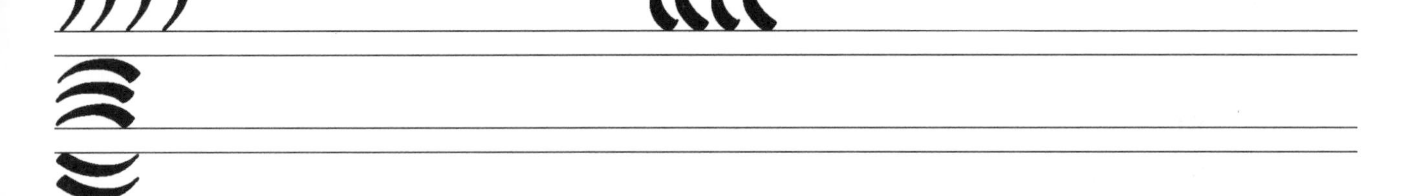

Write the letters *x* and *z*.

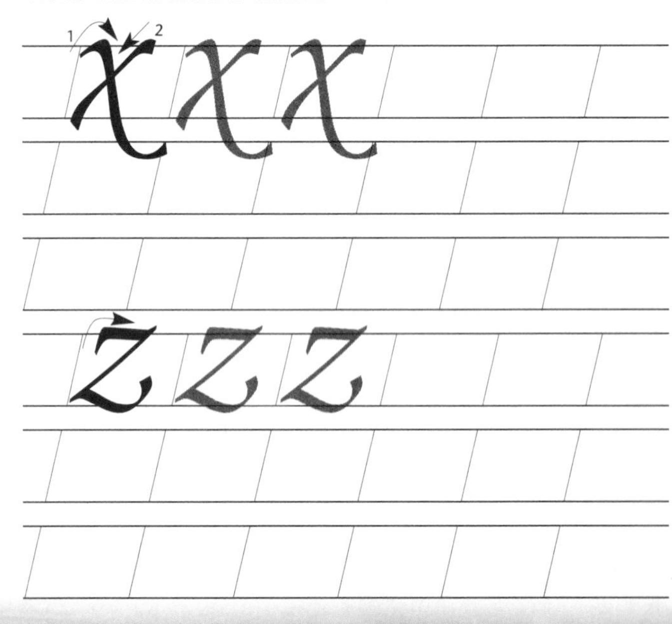

People and Professions

Whosoever therefore shall break one of these least commandments, and shall teach men so, he shall be called the least in the kingdom of heaven: but whosoever shall do and teach them, the same shall be called great in the kingdom of heaven.
—Matthew 5:19

roots

stems

leaves

A Horticulturist's Delight

name____________________

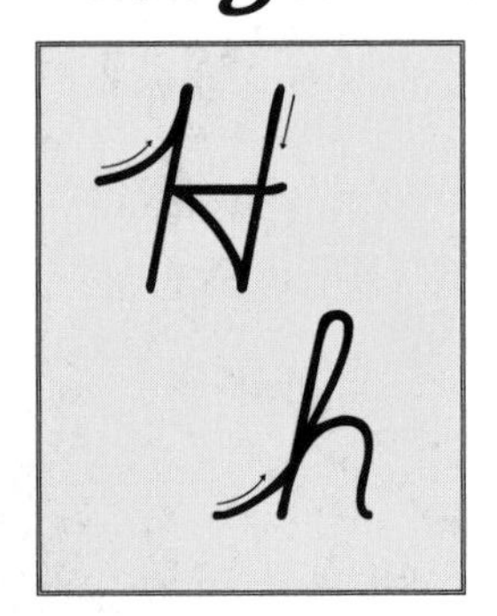

The Missouri Botanical Garden is actually composed of many gardens, including the Climatron, which is a geodesic dome that houses more than a thousand tropical plants.

Listed below are several of the specialized gardens and displays that you could visit. Write the list on handwriting paper.

Climatron
Perennial Garden
Floral Display House
Scented Garden
Mediterranean House
Nursery
Japanese Garden
English Woodland Garden
Vegetable Garden
Desert House
Rose Garden
Linnean House

Missouri Botanical Garden

Kindergarten Fun

name______________________

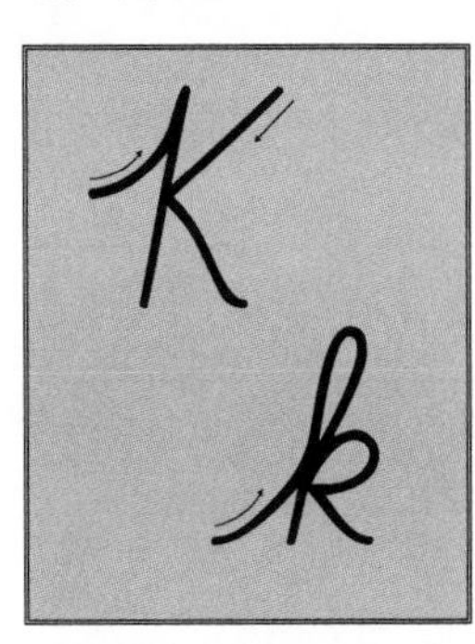

Mrs. Fisher, an experienced kindergarten teacher, uses play dough to help her students learn important basic skills.

Play Dough

2 cups flour
4 tablespoons cream of tartar
1 cup salt
2 tablespoons oil
2 cups water
food coloring

Stir over low heat for approximately three minutes. When the mixture forms a ball, remove from heat. Store in airtight container. Do not refrigerate.

Write Mrs. Fisher's recipe for play dough on the lines below.

Nature's Song

name________________________

Write the letters and words.

H H
h h
horticulturist

K K
k k
kindergarten teacher

Handwriting Tips

When a line of poetry or hymn does not fit on one line, divide the line and indent the second part on the next line.

Write the hymn on handwriting paper.

This Is My Father's World

This is my Father's world,
The birds their carols raise,
The morning light, the lily white,
Declare their Maker's praise.
This is my Father's world,
He shines in all that's fair;
In the rustling grass I hear Him
    pass,
He speaks to me ev'rywhere.

Maltbie D. Babcock

Corel Corporation

Garden Strategy

name________________________

Self-evaluation

	s	n
Posture		
Paper Positioning		
Pencil Hold		
Letter Formation		
Alignment		
Slant		
Spacing		
Neatness		

s=satisfactory n=needs improvement

Brian's uncle is a horticulturist. He helped Brian plan his vegetable garden so that it would produce more this year than it did last year. One thing that Brian learned was to keep tall crops from shading low-growing vegetables, making it possible for all plants to get plenty of sunlight.

On handwriting paper, draw a 4½" x 5" rectangle to represent Brian's garden. Write the names of vegetables on the plot in order of their height, beginning with the tallest plants.

Royal Heritage beans 16"
Sweet Pickling cucumbers 8"
Dwarf Crinkled parsley 9"
Tenderheart beets 12"
Patio Gem tomatoes 3½'
Silver King corn 6'
Krockett's Giant peppers 3'
Midget Cherry radishes 6"
Harvey's Huge tomatoes 4'
Golden Wonder carrots 10"

Calligraphy Letters *b* and *d*

name________________________

b d

Calligraphy Tips 

Plan your work on each line so that ascenders and descenders do not collide.

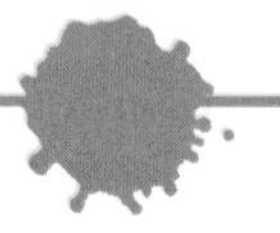

Copy the practice strokes.

Write the letters *b* and *d*.

People and Professions

Sing unto the Lord with thanksgiving; sing praise upon the harp unto our God: who covereth the heaven with clouds, who prepareth rain for the earth, who maketh grass to grow upon the mountains.
—Psalm 147:7-8

A Noble Profession

name________________________

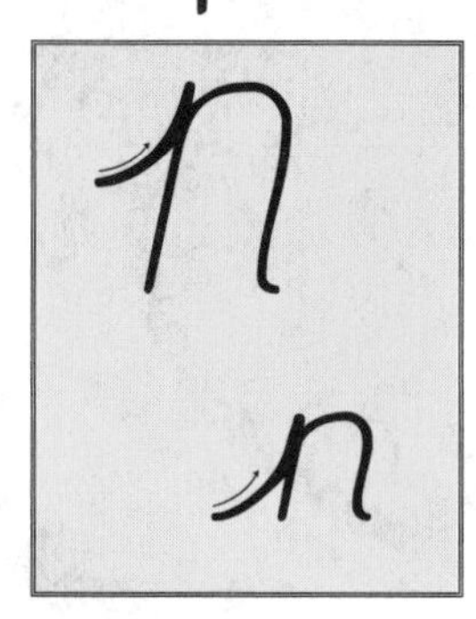

In the 1800s, hospitals were only for the very poor who could not afford nurses in their homes. Since only untrained nurses worked in the hospitals, the patients did not receive proper care. Florence Nightingale trained at the Institution of Kaiserwerth in Germany to become a hospital nurse. She believed that nursing should be a noble profession, and she became devoted to the training of nurses and to the improvement of hospitals and public health.

Write on handwriting paper this list of positions held by today's graduate nurses.

General hospital duty
Private duty
Supervisory nursing
Administrative nursing
Industrial nursing
Nursing education
Public health nursing
Clinic nursing
Anesthetist
Surgical assistant
X-ray technician
Missionary nursing

Florence Nightingale
1820-1910

On the lines below write the quotations by Florence Nightingale.

"I shall succeed because I must."

"Nursing should be a noble profession."

Weather Reporting

name________________________

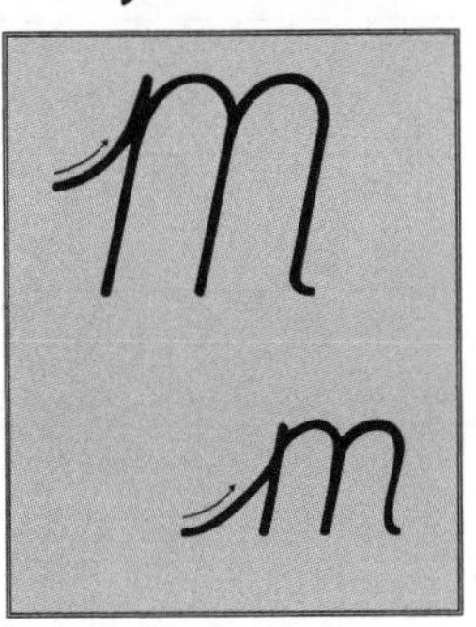

Meteorologists observe the atmosphere and weather and attempt to explain their observations. Weather balloons, satellites, ships, and ground stations are used by meteorologists to gather information about the weather. After the information received from the instruments is recorded, it is sent to a forecast center.

Write the information about the weather instruments on the lines below.

A rain gauge is a large, open metal can that is used to measure precipitation.

____

____

____

An anemometer, a series of cups attached to a vertical pole, is used to measure wind speed.

____

____

____

____

A thermometer, a thin glass tube containing mercury, is used to measure air temperature.

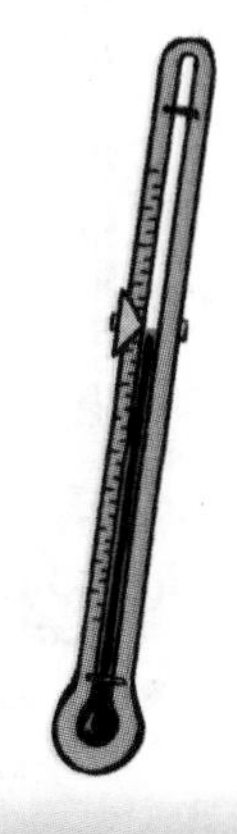

____

____

____

____

The Wind and the Sun

name______________________

Write the letters and words.

n n

n n

nurse

m m

m m

meteorologist

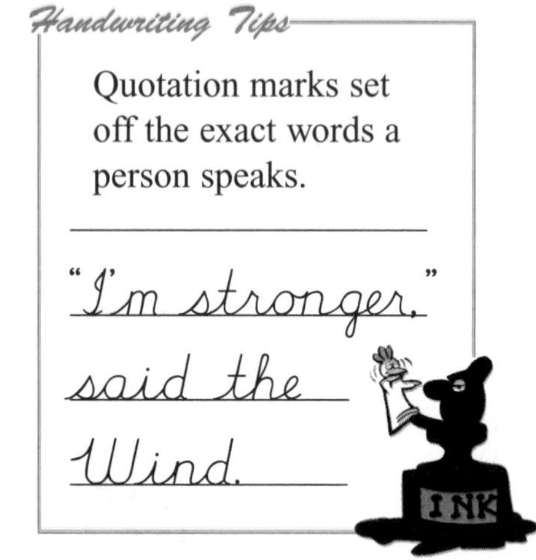

Write the fable on handwriting paper. Include the quotation marks.

One day the Wind and the Sun were arguing about which was stronger. The Wind boasted, "I'm stronger because I can wave a flag, whistle a tune, and sail a ship!"

Soon a traveler came walking down the road. The Sun challenged the Wind, "Whichever of us can force the traveler to take off his coat will be the stronger one. You may try first."

Then the Sun hid behind a cloud, and the Wind began to blow. But the harder he blew, the tighter the traveler wrapped his coat around him.

Finally the Sun shouted, "Stop!"

It was the Sun's opportunity to shine now. And he shone so brightly that the traveler became too hot and had to remove his coat before he could finish his journey.

Moral: Kindness has a greater effect than sternness.

Emergency!

name________________________

Self-evaluation s n

	s	n
Posture		
Paper Positioning		
Pencil Hold		
Letter Formation		
Alignment		
Slant		
Spacing		
Neatness		

s=satisfactory n=needs improvement

The average citizen can be trained to administer first aid like a nurse. First-aid training enables a person to determine the seriousness of an emergency situation and the necessary procedures. There are important rules to follow when giving first-aid treatment.

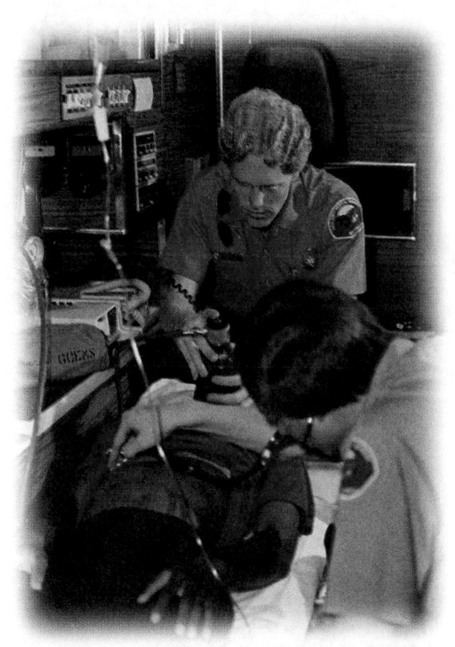

George R. Collins

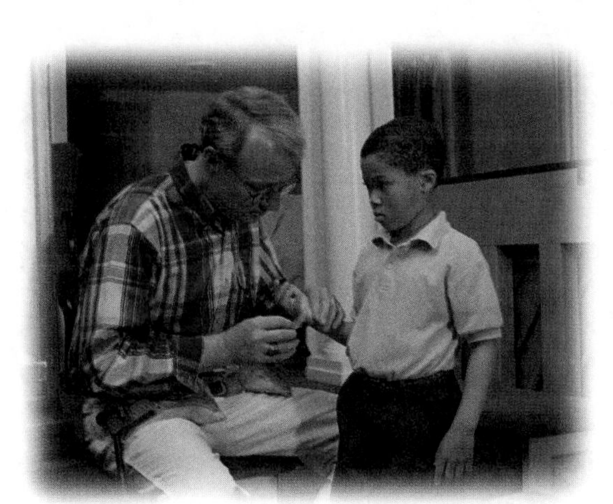

Sam Laterza

Write the first-aid rules on handwriting paper.

1. Remain calm to determine the extent of the victim's injuries and the treatment necessary.
2. Keep the victim lying down and do not move him unless he is in danger.
3. Control any heavy bleeding and cover the victim to prevent shock.
4. Call for a doctor or an ambulance.

Calligraphy Letters f and l

name______________________

Calligraphy Tips 

Use the slant lines on the guide sheet to help you maintain a 13° slant for each letter.

Copy the practice strokes.

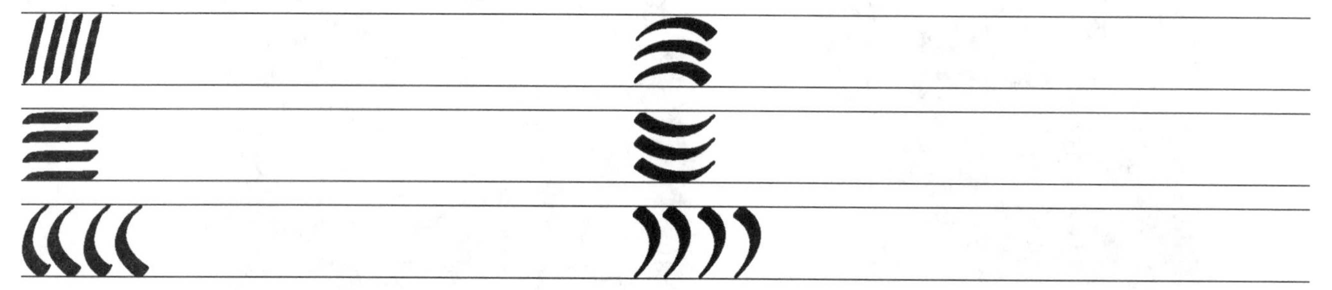

Write the letters *f* and *l*.

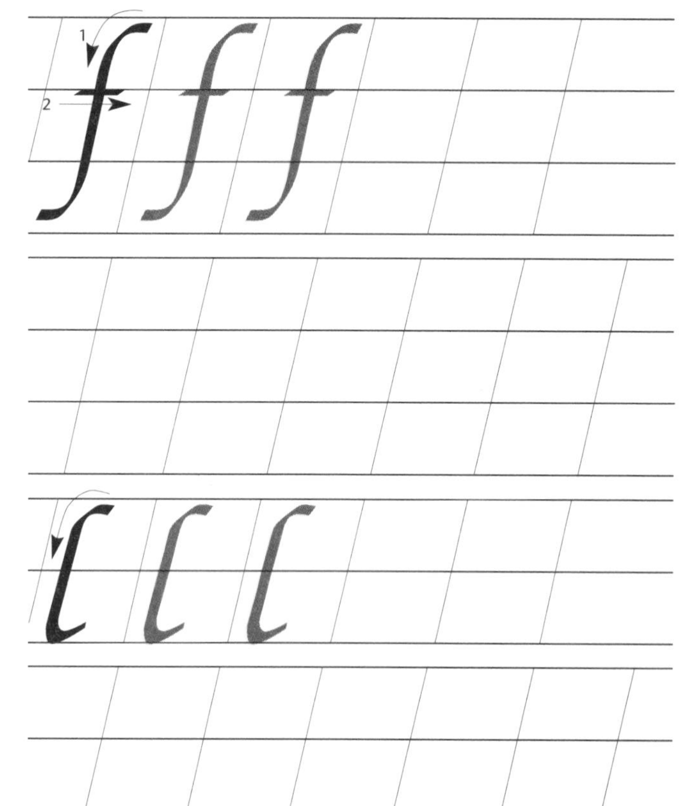

PEOPLE AND PROFESSIONS

And he said unto them, Go ye into all the world, and preach the gospel to every creature.
—Mark 16:15

Ready for Takeoff

name________________________

P p

Pilots of commercial airplanes are fully responsible for passengers, cargo, and mail carried on the plane. The flight engineer, pilot, and copilot work as a team to check the instruments and the condition of the craft before takeoff. Even though commercial airplanes are not military vehicles, they are kept "shipshape" under the authority of the pilot, who is officially in command of his flight.

Write the three paragraphs about the kinds of airplane instruments.

www.arttoday.com

Flight instruments indicate an airplane's speed, its position in relation to the earth's surface, and its planned flight path.

Engine instruments monitor the performance of the engines on the airplane. They indicate the engine's temperature and fuel consumption.

Aircraft systems' instruments are needed to check the electrical, hydraulic, fuel, and air-conditioning systems of the airplane.

Use with Lesson 47.

Sound Waves to Radio Waves

name________________________

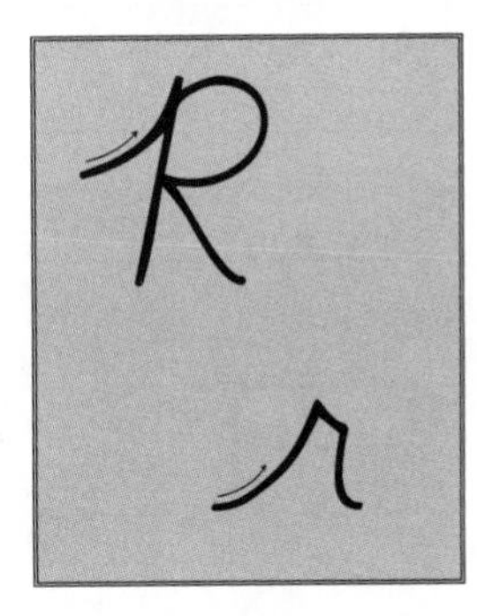

Guglielmo Marconi achieved two great things in his life. He discovered that he could transmit an electric signal across his yard to a receiver he had built. Then he managed to convince unbelieving businessmen to finance his project. With their help, he was able to devote himself to experiments with better equipment and thus developed radio transmitting.

Write the phrases beside the correct pictures and words.

console—amplifies, routes, and mixes audio signals
antenna—sends radio waves into the air
radio—changes the radio waves back into sound
speaker—changes an electrical signal into a sound wave
microphone—changes ordinary sound into electrical waves

Unusual Films

Unusual Films

Unusual Films

PhotoDisc, Inc.

www.arttoday.com

The Spirit of St. Louis

name________________________

Handwriting Tips

The consistency of the slant of letters is important for legible writing.

pilot

pilot

Write the letters and words, using a consistent slant.

P P

p p

pilot

R R

r r

radiobroadcaster

Charles Lindbergh was only twenty-five years old when he made the first solo flight across the Atlantic Ocean in 1927. He flew from Roosevelt Field near New York City to Le Bourget Field near Paris, France, in his single-engine airplane The Spirit of St. Louis. *Lindbergh completed the 3,600-mile flight in 33 1/2 hours.*

Before Lindbergh flew from New York City, he had flown his plane from San Diego, California, to St. Louis, Missouri, and then to New York City. After the historic trans-Atlantic flight, he visited several European cities and three American cities, where he was greeted with celebrations and parades.

www.arttoday.com

On handwriting paper write the names of cities that Lindbergh visited.

San Diego, California
St. Louis, Missouri
New York City
Paris, France
Brussels, Belgium
London, England
Washington, D.C.

Radio Schedule

name____________________

Self-evaluation

	s	n
Posture		
Paper Positioning		
Pencil Hold		
Letter Formation		
Alignment		
Slant		
Spacing		
Neatness		

s=satisfactory n=needs improvement

Missionary radio stations can reach over long distances and inaccessible areas with biblical preaching, teaching, and sacred music as well as news and weather.

Many people are strengthened and blessed in their Christian walk through the radio ministry. Others are saved through the gospel witness.

Doug Garland

Write the radio station schedule on handwriting paper.

6:55 a.m. Sunshine on the Soapsuds
7:00 a.m. World News/Weather
7:05 a.m. ViewPoint
7:10 a.m. Fisherman's Five-Minute Look at the Bible
7:15 a.m. Science, Scripture, and Salvation
7:30 a.m. Word to the World
7:45 a.m. Let the Bible Speak
8:00 a.m. The Anchor of Hope
8:15 a.m. Back to Genesis

Calligraphy Letters
h and *k*

name____________________

h k

Calligraphy Tips 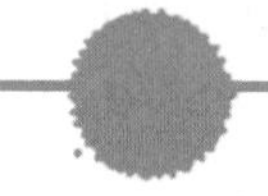

Lift the pen quickly at the end of a letter to avoid inkblots.

Copy the practice strokes.

Write the letters *h* and *k*.

Use with Lesson 51.

PEOPLE AND PROFESSIONS

Are not two sparrows sold for a farthing? and one of them shall not fall on the ground without your Father. Fear ye not therefore, ye are of more value than many sparrows.
—Matthew 10:29, 31

Whose Bones?

name______________________

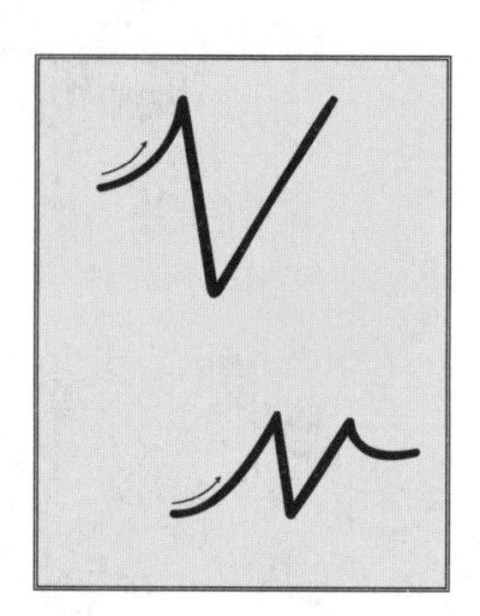

A veterinarian must study hard before he receives his doctor's degree in veterinary medicine (D.V.M.). After two years of preveterinary college training, the student spends at least four more years studying specialized subjects such as anatomy, surgery, and nutrition.

Using the picture below, number the parts of a dog in alphabetical order. Then write the parts alphabetically on handwriting paper.

Works of Art

name________________________

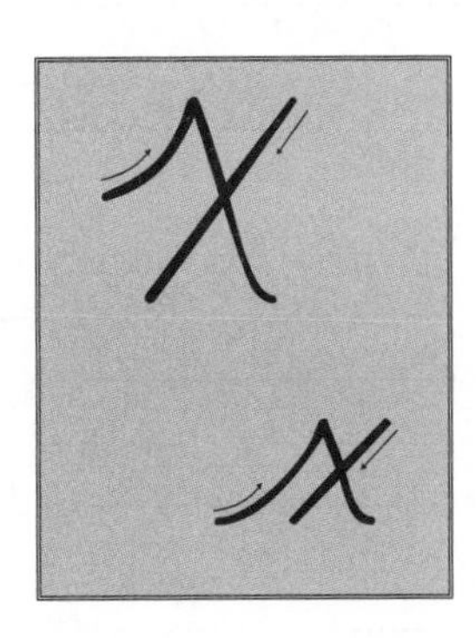

The xylographer often makes woodcuts that are used for beautiful illustrations or prints. After he draws his design onto a block of wood, he cuts away any wood that he does not want to be part of the picture. Next, he applies ink to the wood carving and covers it with a sheet of paper. Slowly and carefully, he rubs the surface of the paper to produce the printed design.

The wood engravings below need titles. After writing the list of titles on handwriting paper, choose one to write in cursive on the lines under each picture.

His Master's Friend
A Quiet Stroll
Look and Live
Dear Old Black

Prize Catch
Beware the Shore
A Fisherman's Dream
Spring Garden

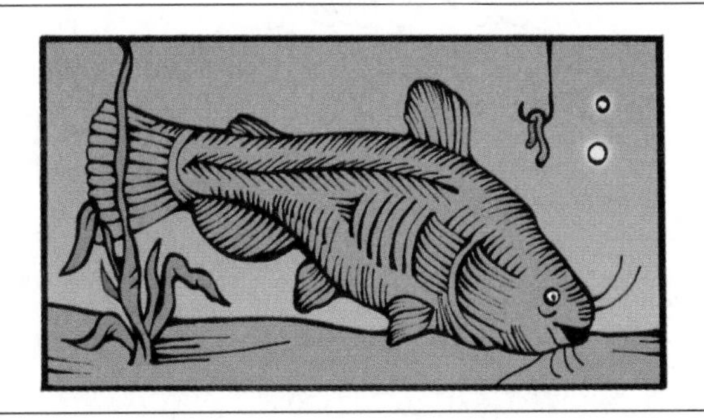

Use with Lesson 53.

Written in Your Hearts

name____________________

Write the letters and words.

V V

v v

veterinarian

X X

x x

xylographer

Write the verse on handwriting paper. Remember to proofread.

"But this shall be the covenant that I will make with the house of Israel; After those days, saith the Lord, I will put my law in their inward parts, and write it in their hearts; and will be their God, and they shall be my people."

Jeremiah 31:33

Rabies Alert

name________________________

Self-evaluation

	s	n
Posture		
Paper Positioning		
Pencil Hold		
Letter Formation		
Alignment		
Slant		
Spacing		
Neatness		

s=satisfactory n=needs improvement

An important part of the veterinarian's work concerns animal diseases that can infect human beings. Rabies is a disease that has been controlled by vaccination to keep it from spreading.

After Rachel's veterinarian friend captured a rabid fox, he sent telegrams to several rabies-control centers. Write the sample telegram on handwriting paper.

PhotoDisc, Inc.

Rabies Control Officer
Any Town
Best State, U.S.A.

Suspect rabid foxes roaming woods, sector 6 of Big Tusk National Park. Suggest inspection of bat colonies in local caves. One case confirmed in sector 5. Please send information on new cases in your area for use in research data. Will keep you informed.

Tom Varnett

Calligraphy Letters p, g, and q

name______________________

p g q

Calligraphy Tips

Refer to the letter models on page 107 to help you avoid making letters that are too thin, too wide, too square, too sharp, or too curved.

Copy the practice strokes.

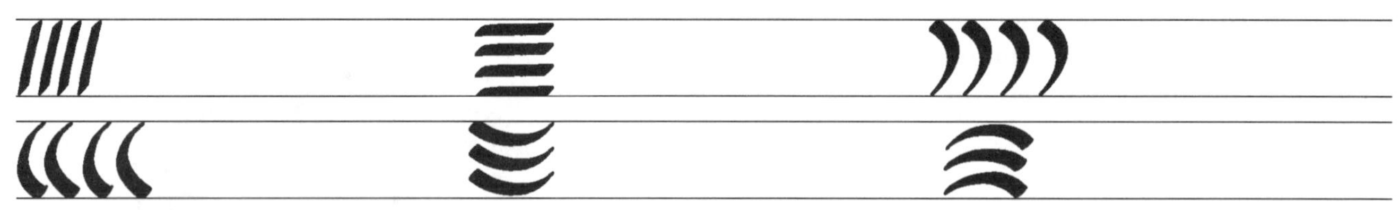

Write the letters *p*, *g*, and *q*.

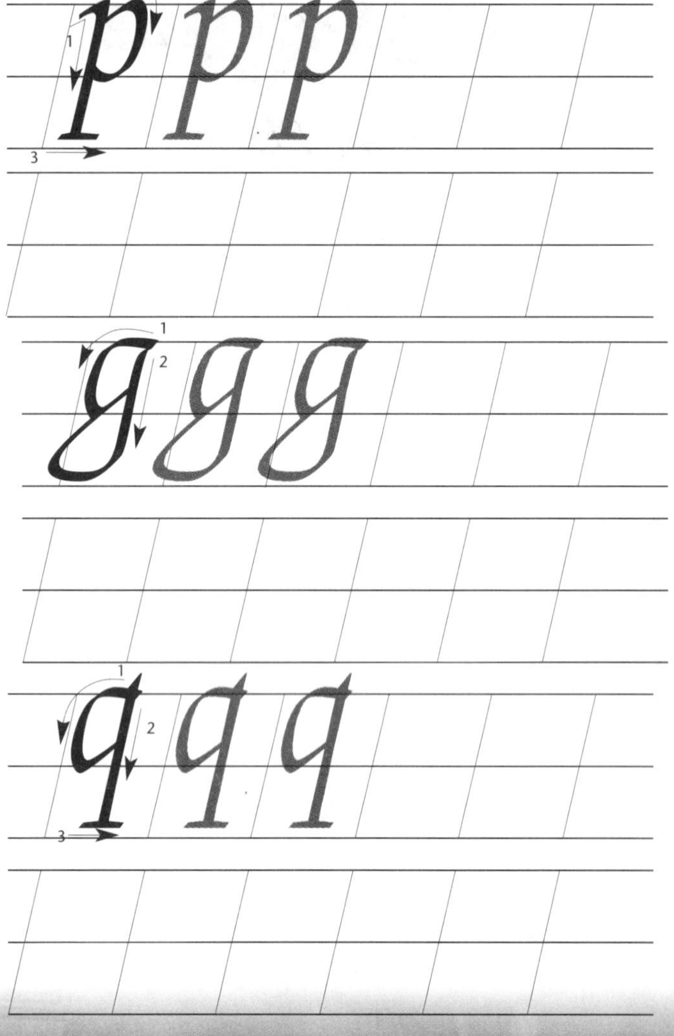

Use with Lesson 56.

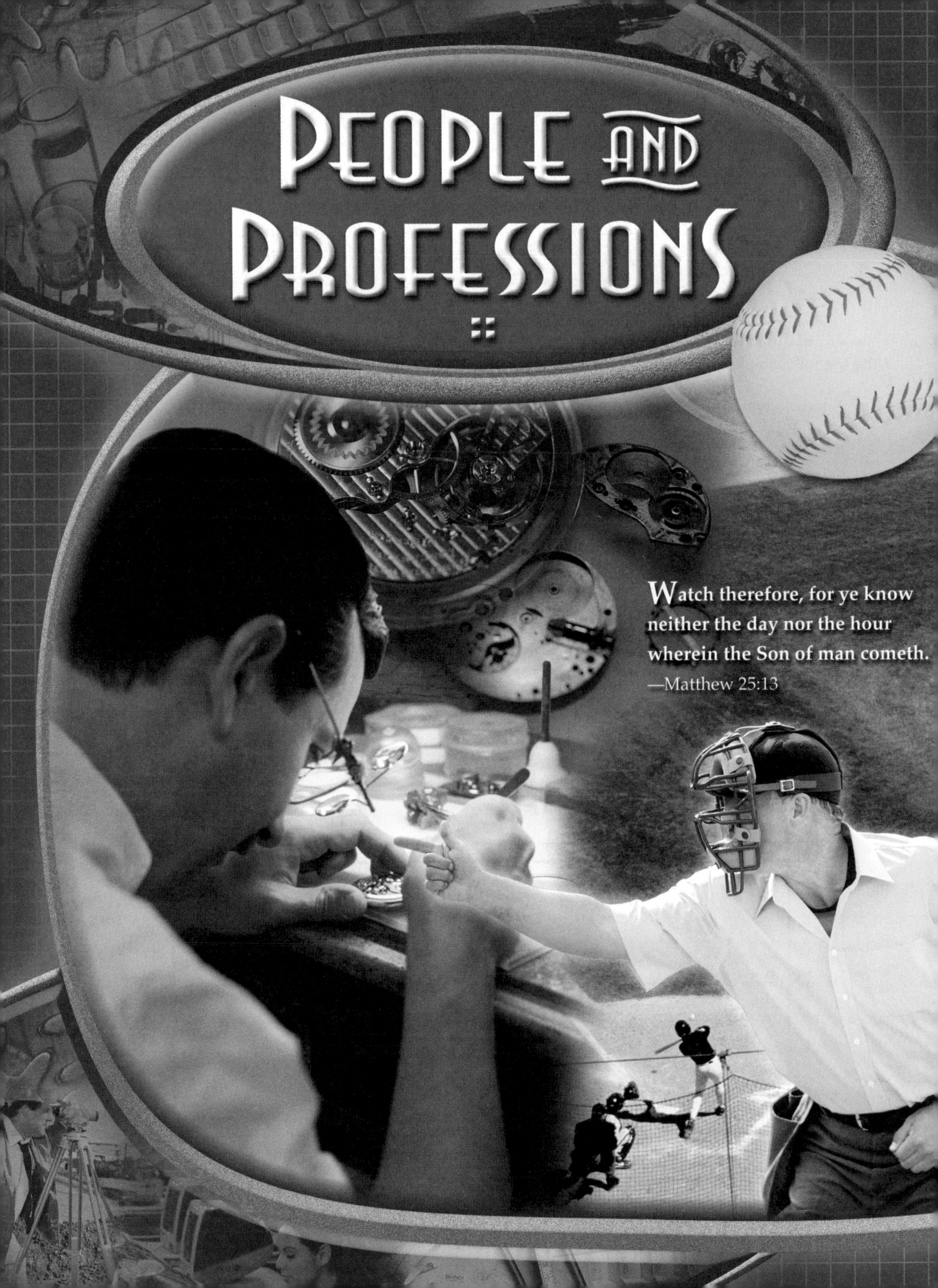

PEOPLE AND PROFESSIONS
Watch therefore, for ye know neither the day nor the hour wherein the Son of man cometh.
—Matthew 25:13

The Very Best

name____________________

The Waltham Watch Company of Massachusetts was famous for its accurate pocket watches. Its pocket watches were adopted by the railroads because of their mechanical precision and durable casing.

Write the following advertisement on handwriting paper.

The Best in
Railroad Watches

In mint condition, this "Vanguard" pocket watch is stem-wound in a gold-filled railroad style case. 15 jewels. Circa 1918. A bargain at $900.

Write the check as Joe Wharton would write it to purchase the watch.

Joseph H. Wharton
Pine Mountain Place
Las Horas, CA

275

____________,20____

67-1
532

Pay to the
Order of ______________________________ $__________

____ Dollars

First
Federal Bank

For ____________________ ____________________

Call It!

name____________________

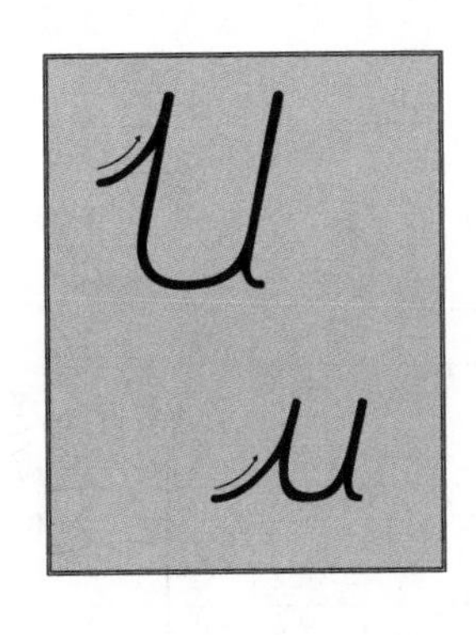

The umpire is an important part of baseball. His main job is to help a game go smoothly while keeping within the rules.

Listed below are several characteristics that some umpires have. Choose the seven good characteristics and write them on handwriting paper.

- is concerned for the safety of the players
- makes decisions calmly and firmly
- is courteous to the coach and players
- won't explain his calls
- gives his best effort
- has a neat appearance
- arrives late for a game
- knows the rules well
- makes calls in favor of the home team
- enjoys the sport

Keeping Time

name________________________

Write the letters and words.

W W

w w

watchmaker

U U

u u

umpire

The Jewish day began at sunset. This chart shows how the Jews of the Bible kept track of time. Use a pen to write the chart in cursive on handwriting paper. If you make a mistake, cross it out neatly.

Our Time	Jewish Term
6:00 P.M.	Sunset
6:20 P.M.	Evening prayer
12:00 A.M.	Midnight
2:00 A.M.	Dog barks
3:00 A.M.	Cock crows
4:30 A.M.	Second cock crows
6:00 A.M.	Sunrise—three blasts of trumpet
	Morning sacrifice
9:00 A.M.	First hour of prayer
12:00 P.M.	Noon
5:40 P.M.	Nine blasts of trumpet
	Evening sacrifice
6:00 P.M.	Sunset
	Six blasts of trumpet on the evening before the Sabbath

PhotoDisc, Inc.

Close Game

name______________________

Self-evaluation

	s	n
Posture		
Paper Positioning		
Pencil Hold		
Letter Formation		
Alignment		
Slant		
Spacing		
Neatness		

s=satisfactory n=needs improvement

Corel Corporation

Number the second column to complete each simile or metaphor. Then write the sentences on handwriting paper under the headings "simile" and "metaphor."

1. Our team moved like	___ tigers on the prowl.
2. The noise from the crowd was like	___ wet spaghetti.
3. The boys on the other team were	___ a volcanic eruption.
4. The other team's pitcher was throwing	___ an old, lame dog.
5. As I walked to the plate, my legs wobbled like	___ a lion's roar.
6. Crack! That ball was	___ bullets at the plate.
7. Our celebration was like	___ a rocket over the fence.

Calligraphy Letters *j* and *y*

name________________________

j y

Calligraphy Tips

Do not breathe! (At least not while making a stroke.)

Copy the practice strokes.

Write the letters *j* and *y*.

People and Professions

And God said, Let the earth bring forth the living creature after his kind, cattle, and creeping thing, and beast of the earth after his kind: and it was so.
—Genesis 1:24

Weigh Anchor!

name____________________

Yy

Below is the map that Yvonne drew while she and her father took a yacht trip from Miami to Key West on the *Yancy*. On handwriting paper make a chart of the places they visited and the distances between them. Show both miles and kilometers.

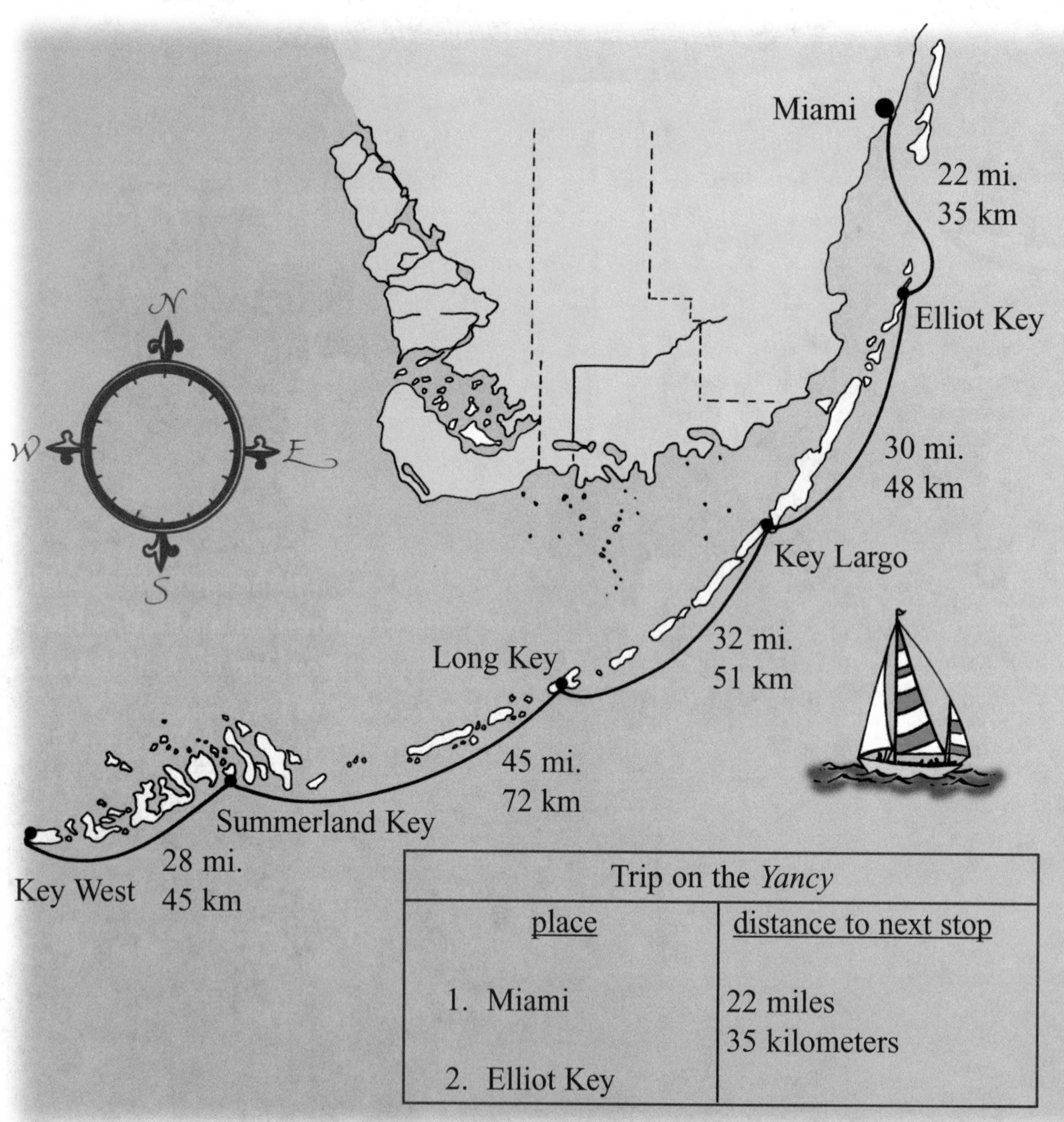

Trip on the *Yancy*	
place	distance to next stop
1. Miami	22 miles 35 kilometers
2. Elliot Key	

Use with Lesson 62.

Then and Now

name____________________

Zz

The main objective of a zoologist is to understand the lives of animals. His work may range from studying a dog's brain cells to reporting on the behavior of giraffes in Africa. Many of the discoveries made by zoologists have given medical researchers valuable information about the human body.

Write the outline below on handwriting paper.

Zoology

I. Ancient collections of animals
   A. Chinese and Egyptian
   B. King Solomon's

II. Scientific study of animals
   A. Books by Aristotle
   B. Animals from other lands
   C. Experiments with animal anatomy

III. Zoology today
   A. Many branches of study
   B. Many careers to choose from

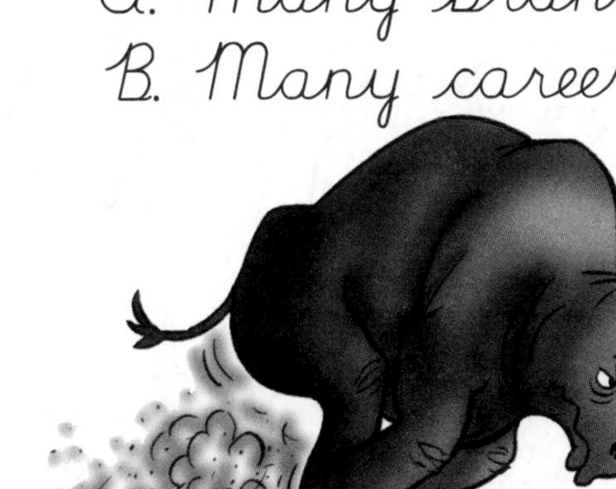

Yvonne's News

name________________________

Write the letters and words.

Y Y
y y
yachtsman

Z Z
z z
zoologist

Handwriting Tips

Don't smudge ink or wrinkle paper. Remember: Neatness counts!

Self-evaluation

	s	n
Posture		
Paper Positioning		
Pencil Hold		
Letter Formation		
Alignment		
Slant		
Spacing		
Neatness		

s=satisfactory n=needs improvement

Write Yvonne's post card to her brother, using handwriting paper. Can you decode the message concealed in the sailboat numbers?

Dear Sam,
Yesterday we stopped to explore and take a swim. I saw a parade of sailboats. They had these numbers: 9421; 721; 161; 1916; 1149; 198; 715; 124; 315; 914.
Love,
Yvonne

postage

POST CARD

Mr. Sam Young
263 Zarvos Place
Florissant, MO
63033

Hint:
1=a
2=b
3=c
etc.

Post-Test

name________________________

Write the quotations from page iv.

Cursive Models

name________________________

Aa Bb Cc

Dd Ee Ff Gg Hh

Ii Jj Kk Ll Mm

Nn Oo Pp Qq Rr

Ss Tt Uu Vv Ww

Xx Yy Zz

1 2 3 4 5 6 7 8 9 0

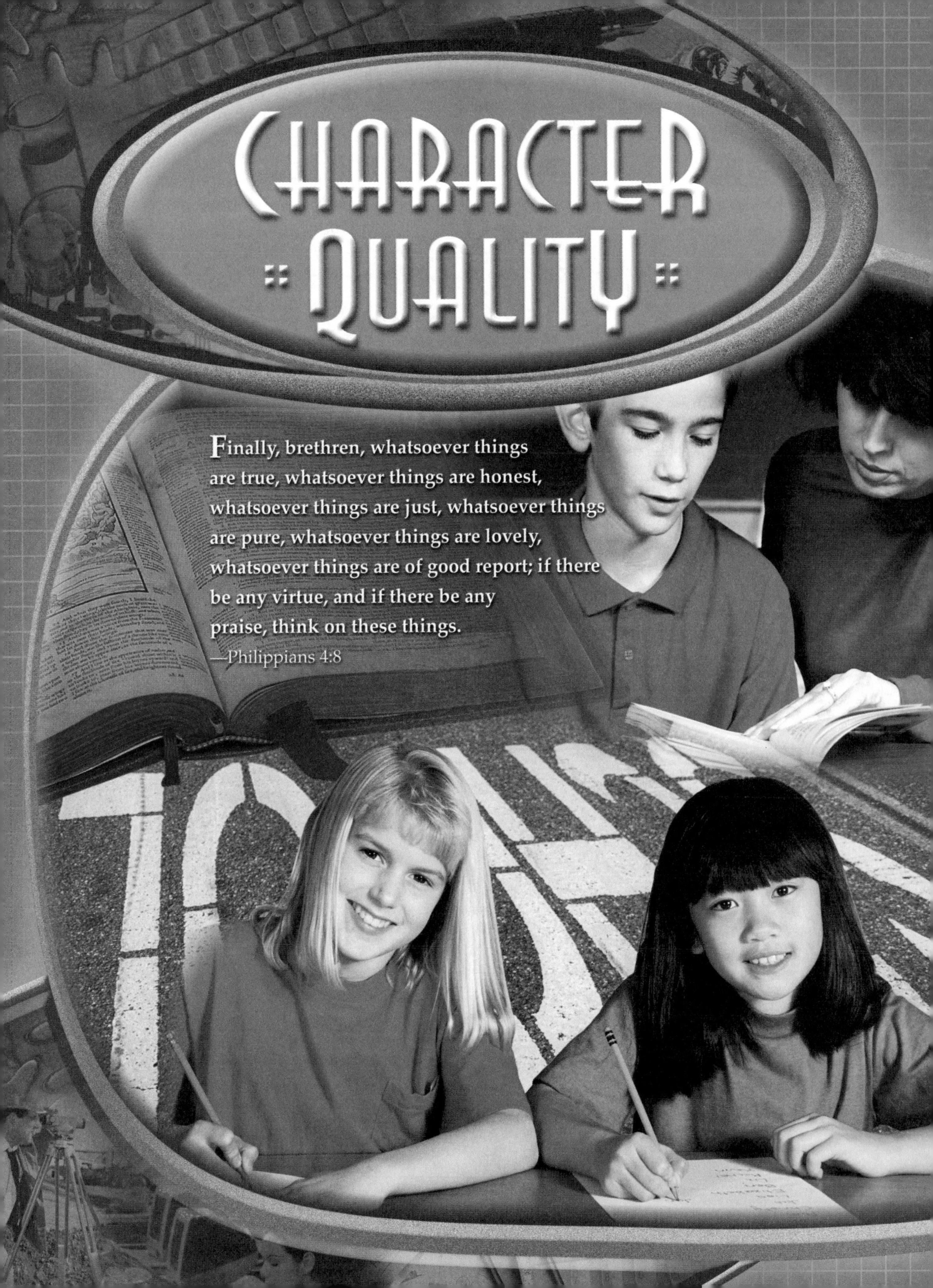
CHARACTER
QUALITY
Finally, brethren, whatsoever things
are true, whatsoever things are honest,
whatsoever things are just, whatsoever things
are pure, whatsoever things are lovely,
whatsoever things are of good report; if there
be any virtue, and if there be any
praise, think on these things.
—Philippians 4:8

Calligraphy Lowercase Review

a b c d e f g h i j

k l m n o p q r

s t u v w x y z

Now Penfellow's speed is much greater,
And his puppet's a good illustrator;
For with nothing to view
(And much writing to do),
The two scribes must do daydreaming later.

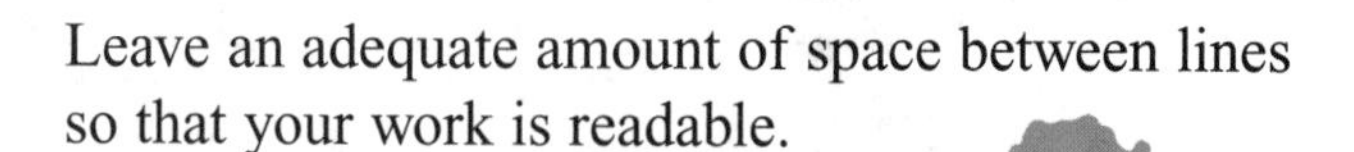

Leave an adequate amount of space between lines so that your work is readable.

Write the following on the lines on page 83.

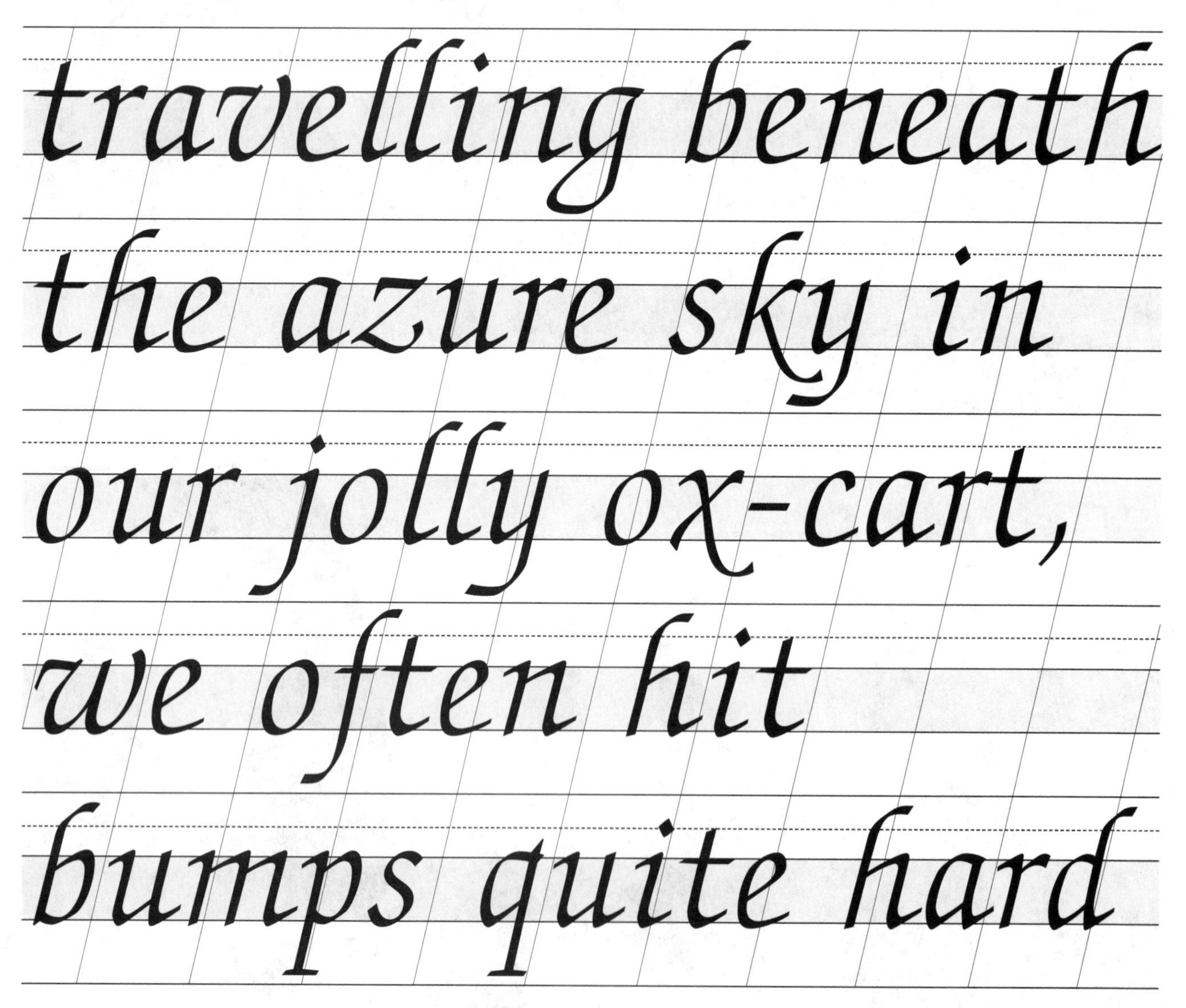

Use with Lesson 66.

Calligraphy Letters *B* and *D*

Write the letters and words.

1 2 *B B*

1 2 *D D*

Blessed

Diligent

Calligraphy Letters *C* and *G*

Write the letters and words.

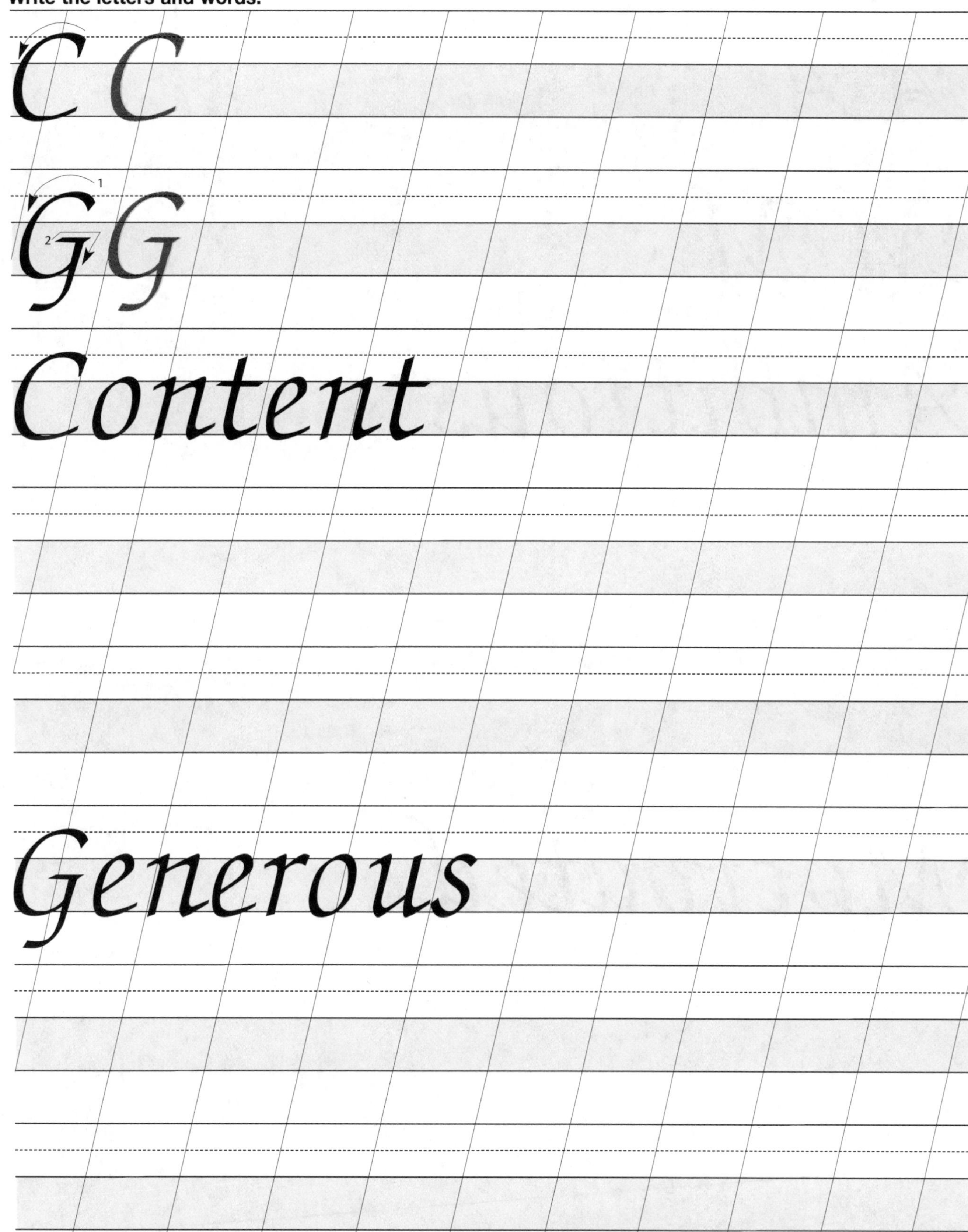

Calligraphy Letters *A* and *M*

Write the letters and words.

Use with Lesson 69.

Calligraphy Letters *E* and *F*

Write the letters and words.

Calligraphy Letters *H* and *K*

Write the letters and words.

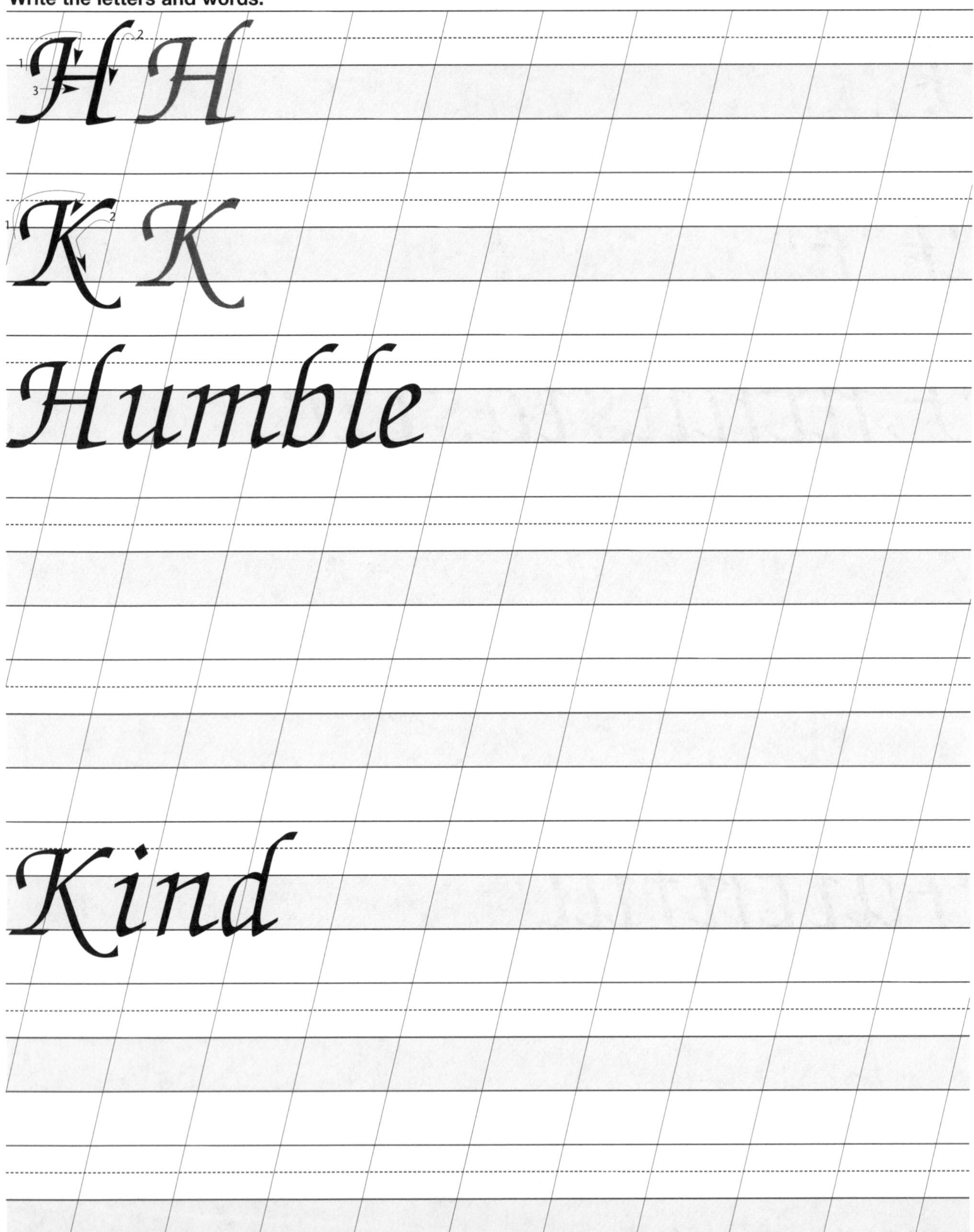

Calligraphy Letters I and J

Write the letters and words.

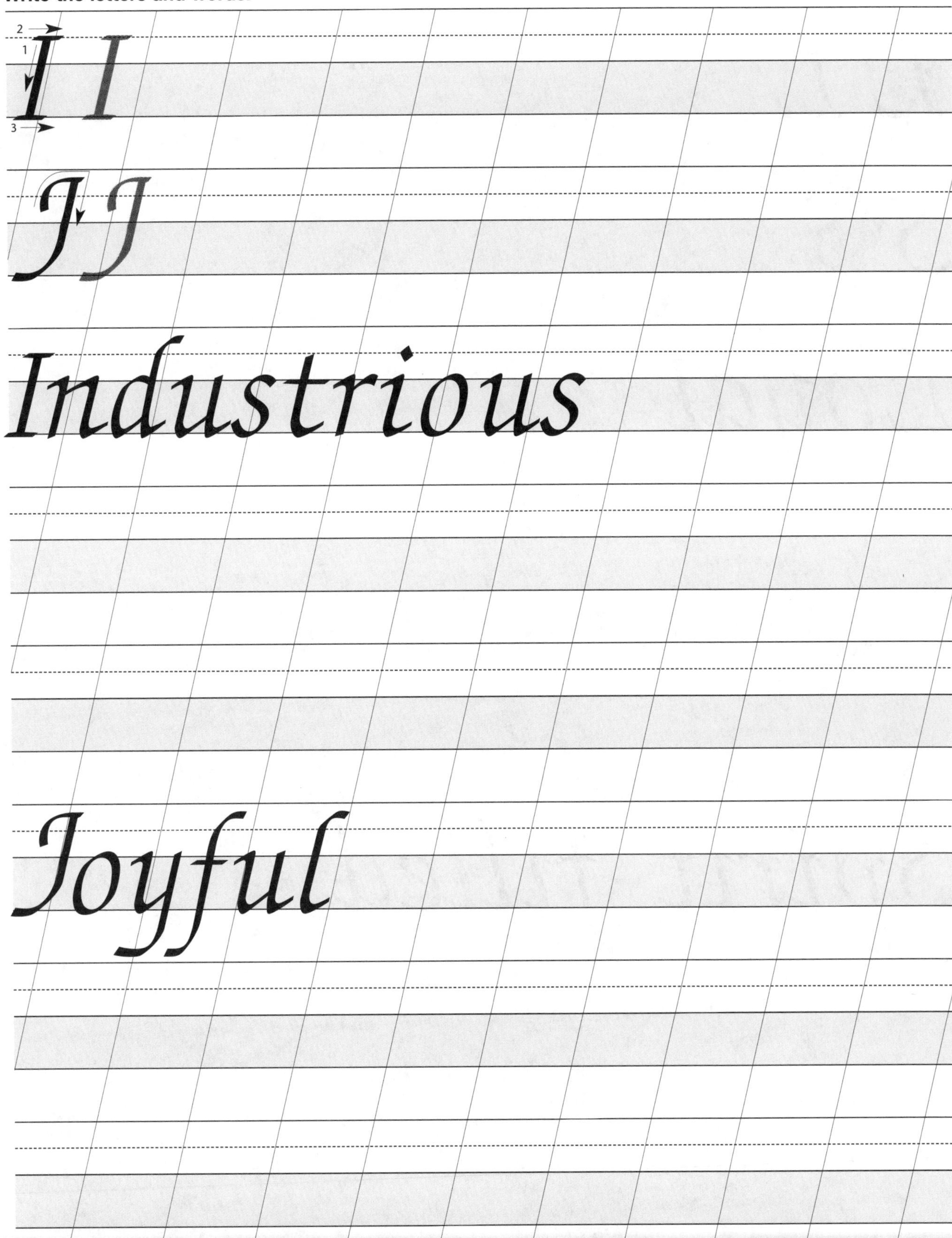

Calligraphy Letters *L* and *S*

Write the letters and words.

Calligraphy Letters *N* and *T*

Write the letters and words.

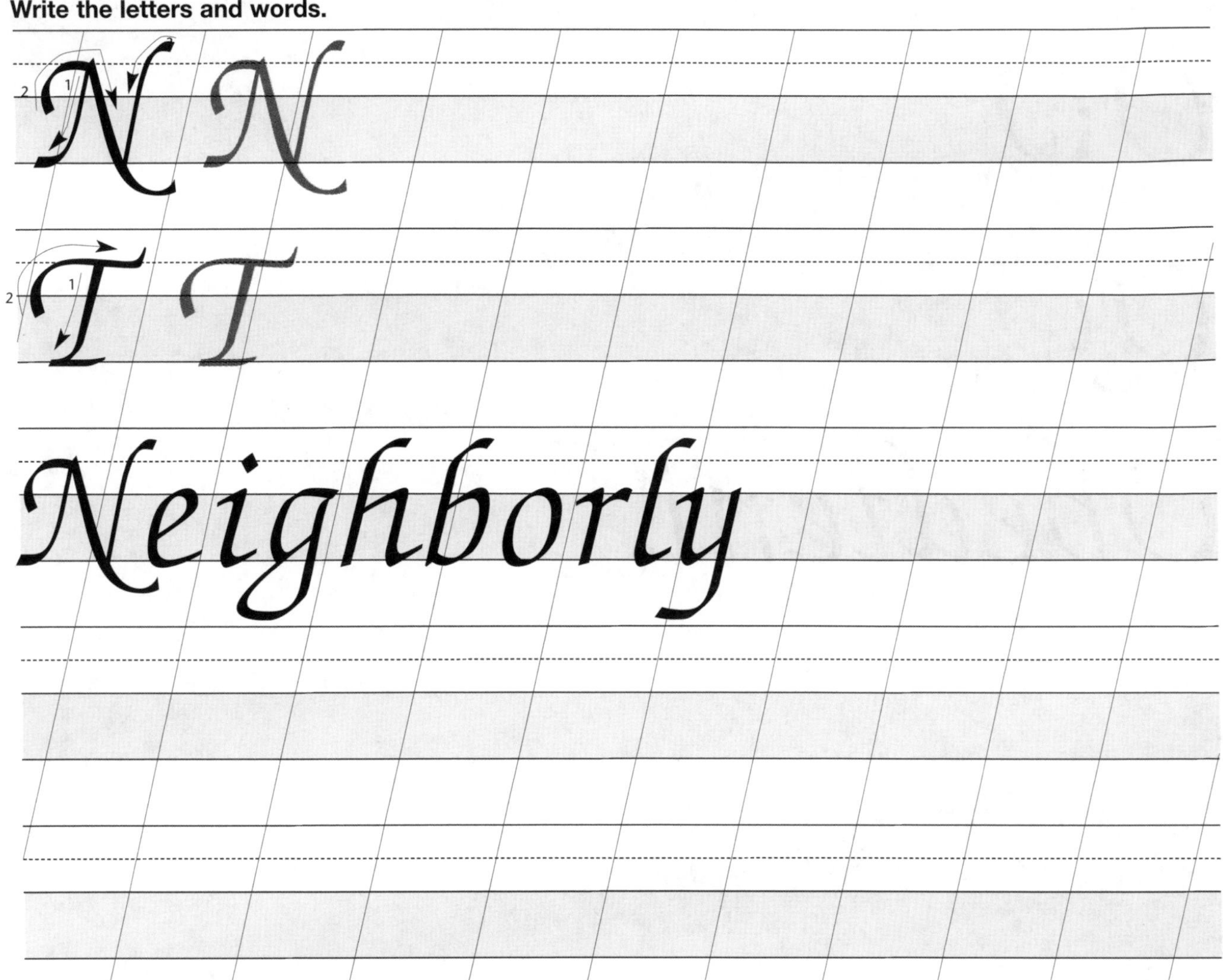

Truthful

Calligraphy Letters O and Q

Write the letters and words.

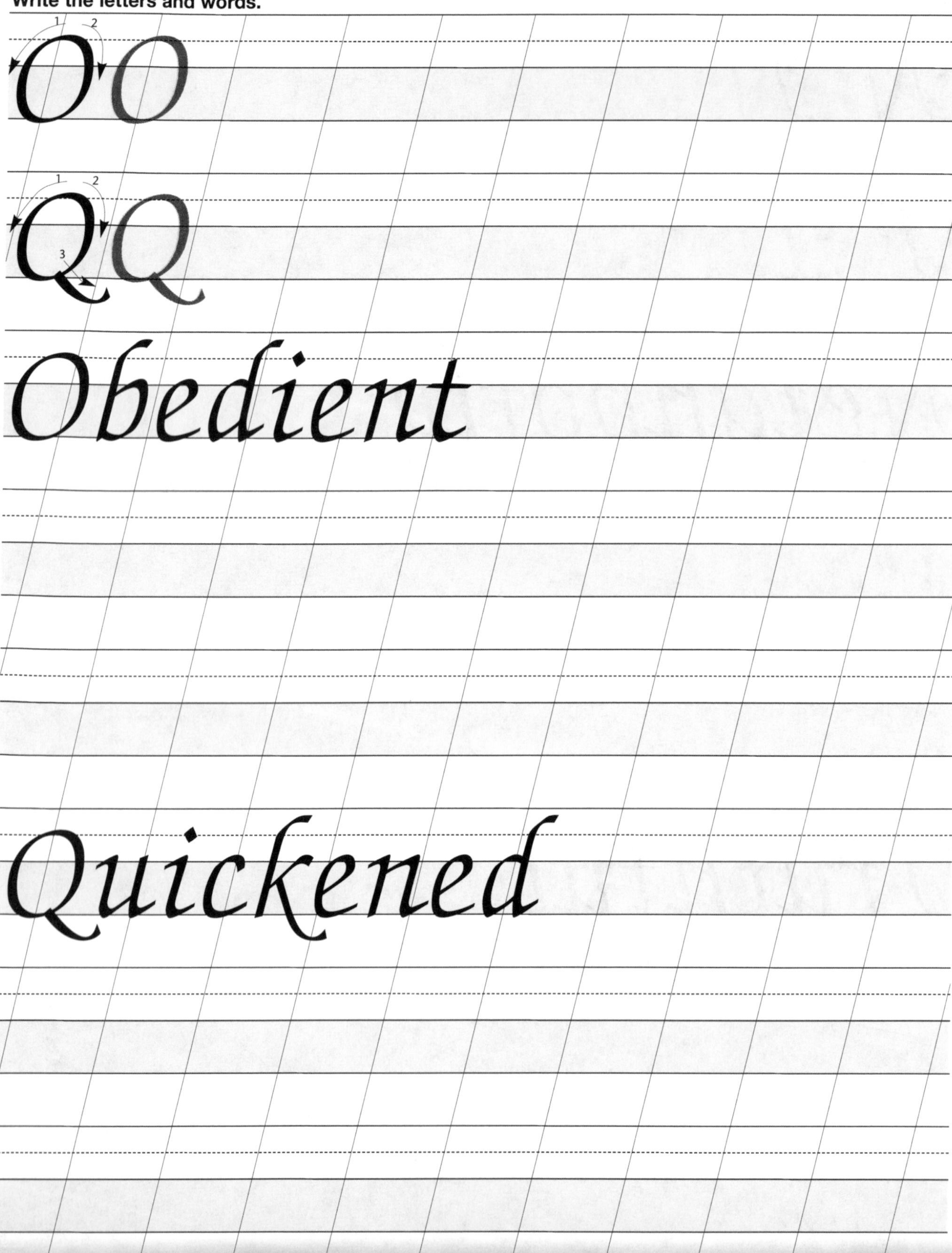

Calligraphy Letters *P* and *R*

Write the letters and words.

P P

R R

Patient

Responsible

Calligraphy Letters *U* and *Y*

Write the letters and words.

U U

Y Y

Unselfish

Yielded

Calligraphy Letters *V* and *W*

Write the letters and words.

Calligraphy Letters X and Z

Write the letters and words.

1 2 X X

Z Z

Xenial

Zealous

Calligraphy Numerals

Write the numerals.

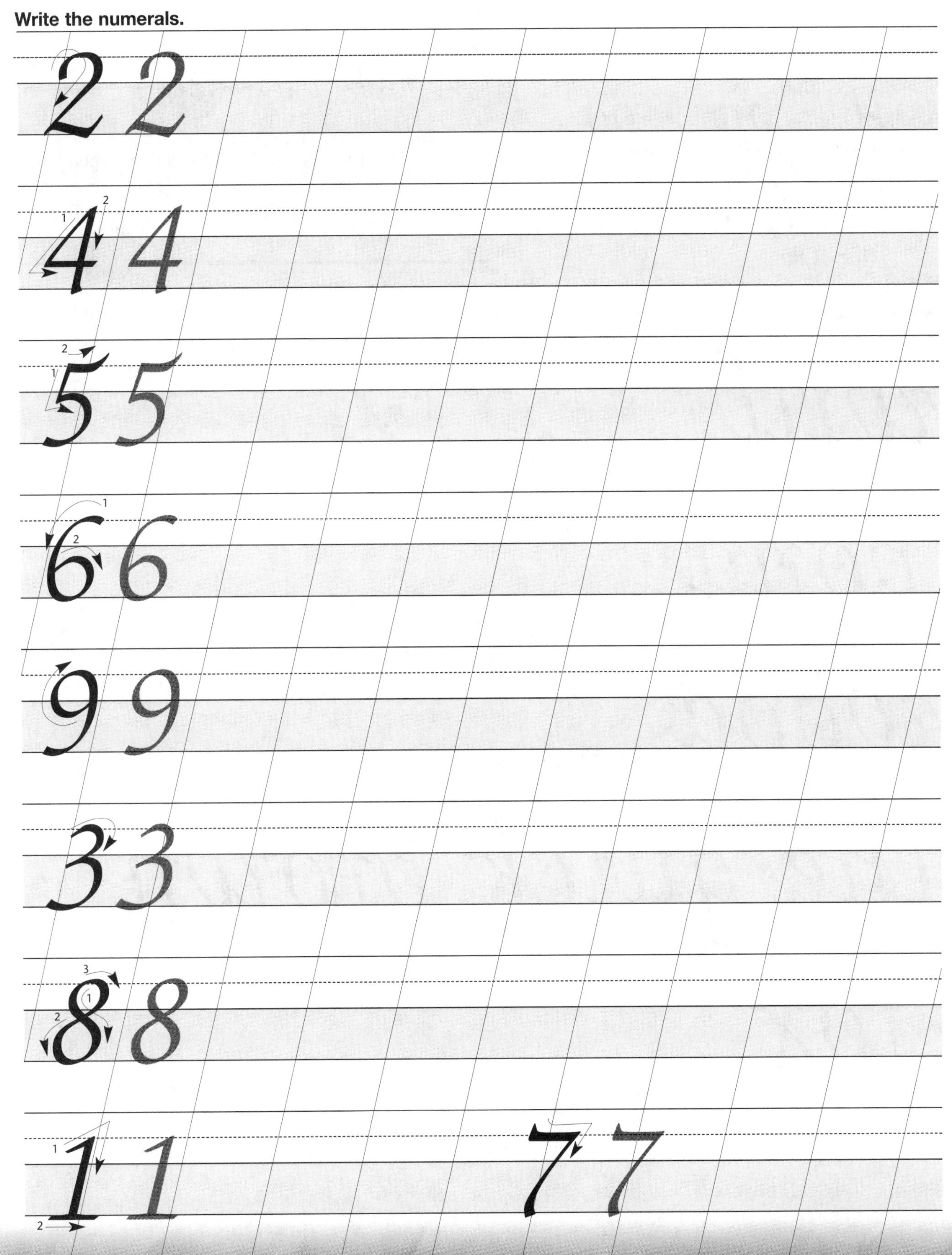

Use with Lesson 80.

Spacing in Calligraphy

spacing between:

il — straight letters

on — curved and straight letters

oo — curved letters

edvaro

Calligraphy Tips 

Use the appropriate amount of space between letters, words, and lines.

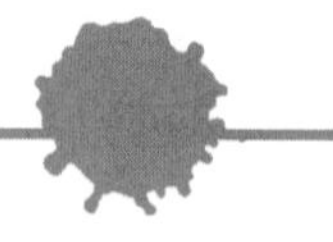

Write the words.

will

pond

wood

the quick brown

fox

Use with Lesson 81.

Layout in Calligraphy

Calligraphy Tips

Plan your layout, leaving margins and allowing room at the end of each line to either finish a word or to break it at a proper place.

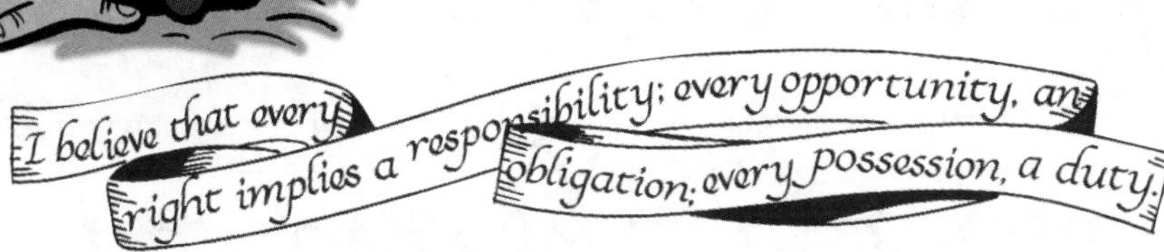

Look at the following layout examples. Decide which example is better and why it is better.

I believe that every right
implies a responsibilit
every opportunity, a
obligation; every
possession,
a duty.

I believe that every
right implies a
responsibility; every
opportunity, an
obligation; every
possession, a duty.

If Jesus Christ
be God and died
for me, then no
sacrifice can be
too great for me
to make for Him.
C. T. Studd

Whether therefore
ye eat, or drink,
or whatsoever
ye do, do all to
the glory of God.
I Corinthians 10:31

He informed me
that he was a
page. "Go 'long,"
I said, "you ain't
more than a
paragraph."
Samuel Clemens

Minor Details

A loosened, muddy,
tennis-shoe string
pulled me quickly
to the ground
and asked me to
give attention to
minor details.

Calligraphy Glossary

alignment The arrangement of letters in a straight line

branch The part of a letter where a curved stroke joins the stem

calligraphy The art of fine handwriting

Chancery cursive A type of italic calligraphy invented by the Italian Ludovico Arrighi in 1522

chisel-point pen A pen which can make broad or thin strokes, depending on the angle of its flat-edged "point" to the horizontal edge of the paper

counter The inside white area of a letter

font The style of alphabet being used

guidelines The five lines on a guide sheet (ascender, capital, body, base, and descender) that indicate the height of each stroke

ascender
capital
body
base
descender

guide sheet A page of guidelines and slant lines that is placed under handwriting paper to direct the height and slant of each stroke

layout The arrangement of lines of calligraphy on a page

pen angle The angle of the chisel point of a pen to the horizontal edge of the paper (For Chancery cursive it is a 45° angle.)

pen width The width of the chisel point of a pen and the width of the stroke it produces

practice strokes The basic strokes of each font used by calligraphers to warm up

serif The short, curved beginning or ending part of a stroke

slant lines The diagonal lines on a guide sheet that indicate the proper angle (13°) of the letter

space The amount of white area between letters, words, or lines

spacing The result of arranging the white area between letters, words, or lines

stem The vertical stroke of a letter

stroke A single mark formed with a pen

x-height The distance between the base and the body lines, equal to five pen widths

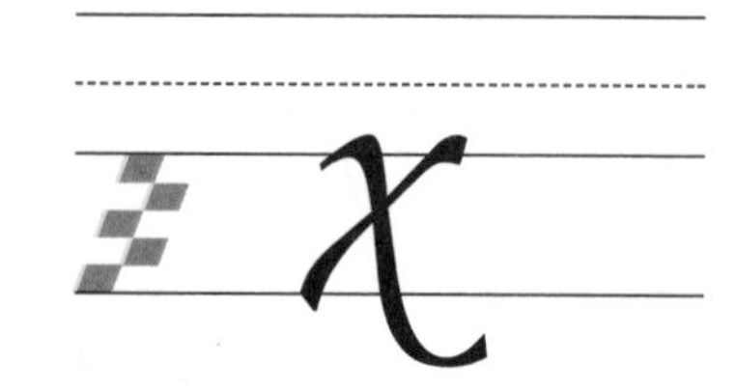

Calligraphy Tips

I. Pen protection
  A. Keep the pen cap on when the pen is not in use.
  B. Do not press too hard on the pen chisel point when writing.
II. Proper positions
  A. Proper body position
    1. Sit up straight.
    2. Keep your feet flat on the floor.
    3. Keep your body facing the desk.

  B. Proper paper position
    1. Line up the bottom of your paper with the edge of your desk. (If you are left-handed, you may want to slant your paper.)
    2. Move your paper to the left as you write across the page. By moving the paper under your hand (and not your hand across the paper), you will be able to keep a consistent pen angle.
  C. Proper pen hold
    1. Hold the pen loosely between your thumb and your first and second fingers.
    2. Rest the pen near the first knuckle.
    3. Hold the pen upright so that it is easier to control.

III. Pointers for pen holders
  A. Letter formation
    1. Hold the chisel point of your pen at a 45° angle to the horizontal edge of your paper.

2. Use the slant lines on the guide sheet to help you keep a 13° slant for each letter.
3. Use a 45° pen angle to start each serif and lift the pen quickly to end each serif.

13° 13° 13° 45° 45° 45°

Dd Ee Ff Ss Tt Aa

4. Perform the strokes in the correct order and start and finish each stroke in the correct place.
5. Use the letters on page 107 as a model to help you avoid making letters that are too thin, too wide, too square, too sharp, or too curved.
6. Breathe only between strokes or between words.

B. Spacing

1. Use the most space between two straight strokes in a word, use a little less space between a straight and a curved stroke, and use the least space between two curved strokes. (It is sometimes possible to overlap serifs or tuck them under another letter.)
2. Leave the space of an "o" between each word. Also, plan the words on a line so that the ascenders and descenders do not collide.

VictoroYield LoyaloKind

3. Leave adequate space between lines so that your work is readable.

C. Layout

1. Plan your margins. Most of the time it is visually more pleasing to have a larger margin at the bottom than at the sides.
2. Allow room to finish a word or to divide it at a proper place.

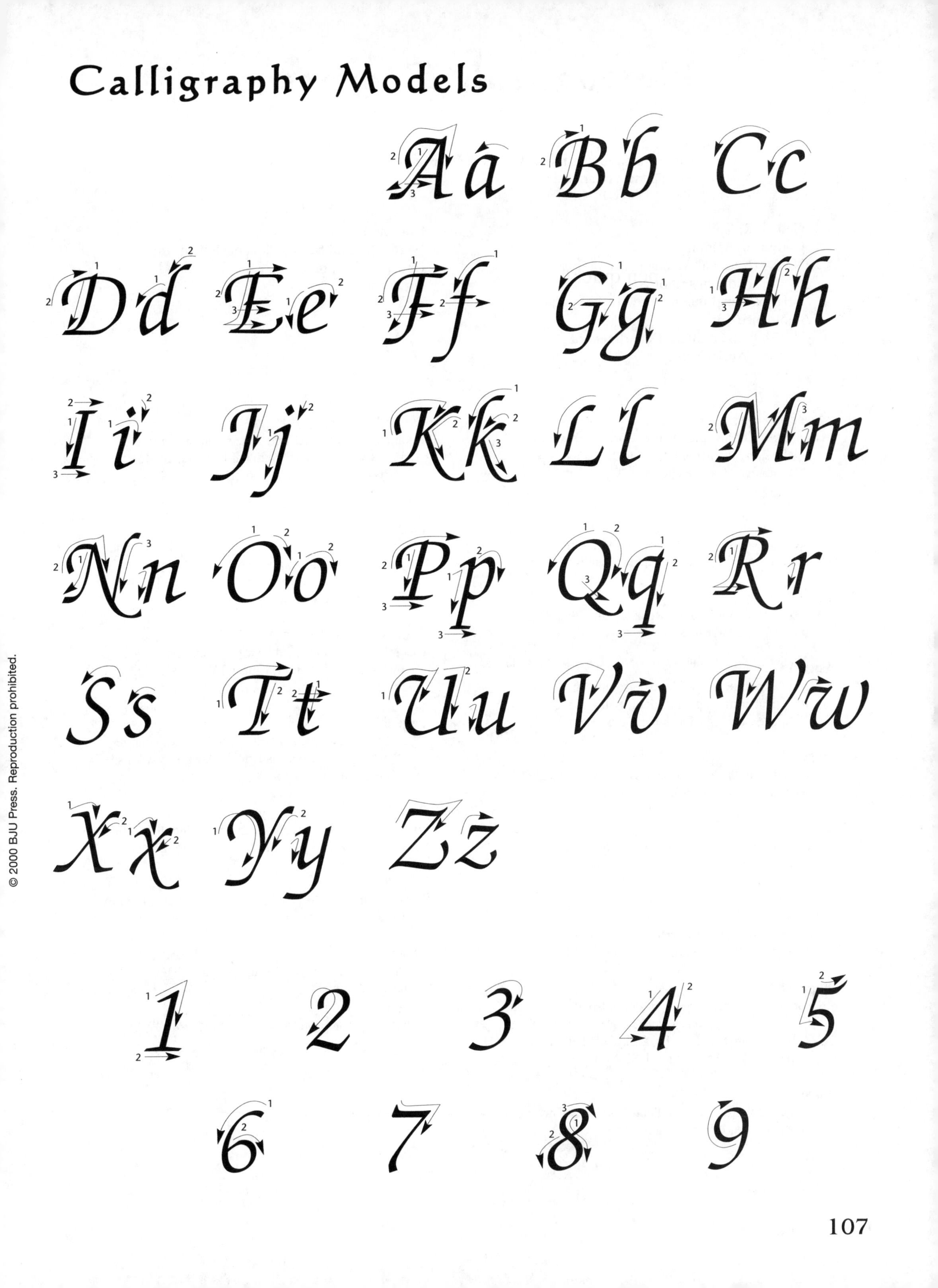

Calligraphy Models

Aa Bb Cc

Dd Ee Ff Gg Hh

Ii Jj Kk Ll Mm

Nn Oo Pp Qq Rr

Ss Tt Uu Vv Ww

Xx Yy Zz

1 2 3 4 5

6 7 8 9

Photograph Credits

The following agencies and individuals have furnished materials to meet the photographic needs of this textbook. We wish to express our gratitude to them for their important contribution.

George R. Collins
Corel Corporation
NASA (National Aeronautics and Space Administration)
NIH (National Institutes of Health)
PhotoDisc, Inc.
USDA (United States Department of Agriculture)
Unusual Films
Ward's Natural Science Establishment, Inc.
Dawn L. Watkins
www.arttoday.com

Cover
George R. Collins: Lighthouse; Corel Corporation: Space stars, Woman pilot; PhotoDisc, Inc.: Astronomer, Gears, Helicopter, Nurse, Satellite dish, Xylographer

Page 3
Corel Corporation: Stars (background); PhotoDisc, Inc.: Astronomer, Calligrapher and calligraphy pen

Page 9
Corel Corporation: Rocks, Rock texture; PhotoDisc, Inc.: Diver, Starfish, Surveyor

Page 15
Corel Corporation: Marble background; PhotoDisc, Inc.: Blueprint, Engineer, Geologist, Quartz; Ward's Natural Science Establishment, Inc.: Gems

Page 21
PhotoDisc, Inc.: Courthouse, Gavel, Inventor, Judge; www.arttoday.com: Invention device

Page 27
Corel Corporation: Toothbrush; PhotoDisc, Inc.: Dentist, Large x-ray, Surgeon; www.arttoday.com: Small x-ray

Page 33
Corel Corporation: Fish background, Fish fly; PhotoDisc, Inc.: Fisherman, Tailor, Thread

Page 39
George R. Collins: Large lighthouse; Corel Corporation: Lighthouse keeper, Small lighthouse, Tulips; PhotoDisc, Inc.: Leaf, Sky; United States Department of Agriculture (USDA): Botanist

Page 45
Corel Corporation: Apples; PhotoDisc, Inc.: Crayons, Horticulturist; Unusual Films: Teacher

Page 51
National Aeronautics and Space Administration (NASA): Hurricane; National Institutes of Health (NIH): Nurse and boy; PhotoDisc, Inc.: Nurse; Unusual Films: Meteorologist

Page 57
Corel Corporation: Woman pilot; National Aeronautics and Space Administration (NASA): Cockpit; PhotoDisc, Inc.: Helicopter, Radio tower; Unusual Films: Radiobroadcasters

Page 63
Corel Corporation: Wood background; PhotoDisc, Inc.: Cat, Veterinarian; Unusual Films: Carving tools, Xylographer lady, Xylographer man

Page 69
Corel Corporation: Baseball; Digital Stock: Umpire; PhotoDisc, Inc.: Baseball field; Dawn L. Watkins: Watchmaker and watch

Page 75
Corel Corporation: Yacht, Yachtsman; PhotoDisc, Inc.: Lion cub, Zoologist; www.arttoday.com: Zoo

Page 81
PhotoDisc, Inc.: Boy and teacher, Girls, School road; Unusual Films: Open Bible

PhotoDisc, Inc.: Green collage on all People and Professions unit openers and purple collage on Character Quality

Photos on inside pages are credited individually.